SPOTLIGHT™ on MUSIC

PIANO ACCOMPANIMENTS

Grade 2

Series Authors

Judy Bond
René Boyer
Margaret Campbelle-Holman
Emily Crocker
Marilyn C. Davidson
Robert de Frece
Virginia Ebinger
Mary Goetze
Betsy M. Henderson
John Jacobson
Michael Jothen
Chris Judah-Lauder
Carol King
Vincent P. Lawrence
Ellen McCullough-Brabson
Janet McMillion
Nancy L.T. Miller
Ivy Rawlins
Susan Snyder
Gilberto D. Soto

Kod

Macmillan McGraw-Hill

NOTE TO THE TEACHER

You asked for it—you got it! Now, for the first time ever, the new piano arrangements for Spotlight on Music™ replicate the vocal and instrumental arrangement on the song recordings. This time-saving feature ensures a seamless transition from the recorded performance to the classroom experience with respect to the harmonic structure, from, and style of the song.

For support in teaching choreography, use the following segments from the Grade-Level DVD:

- **John Jacobson**, which demonstrates selected songs' choreography in front, back, and split screen views.
- **Music Theatre International**, in which Broadway for Kids choreography is presented in several formats, including a slower tempo and a teaching segment of specific choreography details.

The Grade-Level DVD booklet offers additional support with a glossary of choreographed movements and terms related to stage movements.

Choreography notes for the songs in the Broadway for Kids musical are provided by Music Theatre International. Choreography notes for all other songs are written by John Jacobson.

The McGraw·Hill Companies

Published by Macmillan/McGraw-Hill, of McGraw-Hill Education, a division of The McGraw-Hill Companies, Inc., Two Penn Plaza, New York, New York, 10121

Printed in the United States of America

ISBN: 0-02-295857-6

4 5 6 7 8 9 066 09 08 07 06 05

In the Spotlight Contents

Do-Re-Mi
from the movie *The Sound of Music*

PUPIL'S PAGE C

Lyrics by Oscar Hammerstein II
Music by Richard Rodgers
Piano Accompaniment by Tom Anderson

thread,
La, a note to fol-low sew,
F
D7
G
Tea, a drink with jam and bread,
That will bring us
E7
Am
C7
F
Dm7
1.
back to do - oh - oh - oh!
2.
bring us back to
G7
C
G
F
Dm7
G7
doe!
Do - re - mi - fa - so - la - ti - do!
C
C7
F
Dm7
G7
C

Patriotic Medley

PUPIL'S PAGE H

Words by George M. Cohan, Woody Guthrie,
and Katharine Lee Bates
Piano Accompaniment by Mark Brymer

2.
blue, Where there's nev - er a boast or brag. But should auld ac -
F Am D Gm C7 F
quain - tance be for - got, Keep your eye on the grand old flag.
C D♯dim C C7 G7 C7 F
This land is your land, this land is
walk - ing that rib-bon of
F E♭ F B♭

my land From Cal - i - for - nia to the New York Is - land.
high - way, I saw a - bove me that end - less sky - way.
F
C7
F
From the red - wood for - est to the Gulf Stream wa - ters,
I saw be - low me that gold - en val - ley.
F
B♭
F
1.
2.
This land was made for you and me. As I was A -
C7
F

mer - i-ca! A - mer - i-ca! God shed His grace on thee. And
B♭ E♭/F F Cm7 F E♭ F7 B♭ B♭7
crown thy good with broth - er-hood, From sea to shin-ing sea! And crown thy good with
E♭ B♭ E♭ F7 B♭ B♭7 E♭
broth - er-hood, From sea to shin - ing sea!
B♭ E♭ B♭ F7 B♭

Step into the Spotlight

Bring light (on) from low to high, directly at the audience
rush - ing riv - er free, there's mu - sic all a -
hope that's shin-ing bright. So sing out strong, A -
Gm/F
F/E♭ E♭
Dm 7
Gm 7
G♭
Bring light down, directly at audience
round us, there's mu - sic in you and me!
mer - i - ca, and step in - to the light!
A♭9
Cm 11
F 7
Refrain
Light to shoulder
Light overhead
Bring light down directly at audience
Come on and step in - to the spot - light! Come on and
F 7
B♭
Fm 9
B♭7
Light to shoulder
Light overhead
Wave light
L
R
L
R
step in-to the spot - light! Let it shine, shine, shine on our
E♭
C 9/B♭
C 9
B♭/F
D 7/F♯
Gm
Gm/F

Point light, high to low, directly at audience
Light to shoulder
Light overhead
mu - sic and our song. Come on and step in - to the spot -
B♭/C
C
F7
B♭
Fm9
Light to shoulder
Light overhead
Wave light
L
R
- light! Come on and step in - to the spot - light! Let it shine! Let it
B♭7
E♭
C7
B♭/F
Gm
L
R
Point light high to low
To Coda
Rainbow ripple light from L to R
shine on ev - 'ry - one!
cm9
F9
B♭
B♭
Light to face in peel-off groups
1
2. In a world of sound and col - or, in a
F7
B♭
Cm/B♭

*Alternatively, repeat light movements

Bring both hands down toward audience with palms up
L
R
shine on our mu - sic and our song.
Come on and
Gm
Gm/F
C
F
* Step forward L
Clap and dig R foot behind L
Step back R
Step together L
Step upstage L
Touch R foot
Step forward R
Touch L
Step forward L
Clap and dig R foot behind L
Step back R
Step together L
step in - to the spot - light! Come on and step in - to the spot -
B♭
Fm9
B♭7
E♭
C9
Step upstage L
Touch R foot
Wave jazz hands
L
R
L
R
L
- light! Let it shine! Let it shine on ev - 'ry - one!
B♭/F
Gm
C9
F9
B♭
B♭/G
Wipe back of head with R hand
Reach R jazz hand or flashlight high overhead
E♭9/F
B♭

This Little Light of Mine

PUPIL'S PAGE F

African American Spiritual
Piano Accompaniment by Tom Anderson

Lower hands
let it shine,
let it shine.
G
D7
G

A la rueda de San Miguel
(To the Wheel of San Miguel)

PUPIL'S PAGE 60

Traditional Mexican Folk Song
Piano Accompaniment by Dean Crocker

(2.) * insert any name

Ach, du lieber Augustin
(The More We Get Together)

PUPIL'S PAGE 35

German Folk Song
Piano Accompaniment by Dean Crocker

1.
Au - gus - tin. Ach, du lie-ber Au - gus - tin, Al - les ist hin! The
your friends. The more we get to-geth - er, the hap - pier we'll
F
C7
F
2.
be!
F
B♭
Gm7 C7
F

All Around the Buttercup

PUPIL'S PAGE 210

American Folk Song
Piano Accompaniment by Dean Crocker

2.
Em9
A7
D
G/A
D
mf
Bm7
Em7
A7
3.
D
G/A
D
Bm7
Em9
A7
D

America

PUPIL'S PAGE 338

Music by Henry Carey
Words by Samuel F. Smith
Piano Accompaniment by Tom Anderson

Scoop L hand to chest level
Scoop both hands over head
Land of the Pil - grim's pride, From ev' - ry moun - tain-side
C7
F
Clap hands together and bring to heart level
Let free - dom ring.
B♭
F
C7
F

Ani Purim
(Purim)

Animal Fair

PUPIL'S PAGE 214

American Folk Song
Piano Accompaniment by Dean Crocker

Hands to cheeks like "Home Alone"
Shrug
to Coda
trunk. The el - e - phant sneezed and fell on her knees, and what be-came of the
C
G7
G7
"Home Alone" again
monk?
C
f
G7
C
D.S. al Coda
C
G7
C

Coda
monk?
C
G9
C

Apple Picker's Reel

PUPIL'S PAGE 343

Words and Music by Larry Hanks
Piano Accompaniment by Dean Crocker

B♭6
C7
F
C7sus
C7
F
F/A
D.S. al Coda
B♭6
Bdim
C7
Gm7/C
C7
F
B♭/C
F
Coda
ap - ple tree.
F
B♭/C
F
F
mf
Gm7/F
Fmaj7
Gm7/F
F
B♭/F
F

Artichokes

PUPIL'S PAGE 314

Words and Music by Malvina Reynolds
Piano Accompaniment by Dean Crocker

com - for - ta - ble there, they like the san - dy bot - tom and the cool salt air.
G D D Bm7 Gmaj7 A D
Refrain
Ar - ti - chokes Mmm mmm Ar - ti - chokes Mmm mmm
D G D D A7 D
Verse 2
Ar - ti - chokes Mmm mmm When you eat an ar - ti-choke you
D A7 D D Bm
take a lit - tle bite, Stick you in the fin - ger if you don't hold it right.
G D D Bm A7 D

*Reprise of Refrain is written as D.C. al Fine in Student Book.

Australia's on the Wallaby

PUPIL'S PAGE 106

Australian Folk Song
Piano Accompaniment by Dean Crocker

whiz - zing round, The din - go scratch - es grav - el. The pos - sum bear and ban - di - coot are
F
Dm
C7
F
Gm
F/A
all up - on the trav - el.
C7
F
F5/B♭
B♭5/G
F

Away for Rio

PUPIL'S PAGE 170

American Sea Chantey
Piano Accompaniment by Dean Crocker

Ri - o! So fare ye well, my bon - ny young friend, We are bound for Ri - o
D
G
D/F♯
A7sus
Bm
D/A
A7
1., 2.
3.
Grande!
2. We've a
3. Oh,
Grande!
D
A7
D
G/D
D
D
G sus2/D
D
G sus2
D(sus2)

Baby Beluga

PUPIL'S PAGE 26

Words and Music by Raffi and D. Pike
Piano Accompaniment by Dean Crocker

Refrain
Pretend to rock a baby in both arms L R L R
Reach both arms overhead with palms in like a big shrug
Repeat last two measures
Ba - by be - lu - ga. Oh, ba - by be - lu - ga.
Ba - by be - lu - ga. Oh, ba - by be - lu - ga.
Ba - by be - lu - ga. Oh, ba - by be - lu - ga.
B♭
F
v1: Shrug L
v2: Clasp opera hands
v3: Shrug L
Shrug R
Swing opera hands L R L R
Shrug R
Shimmy jazz hands by the side of your face.
Reach both hands to audience, the R hand to ear.
Stretch like you're just waking up
(Last time repeat Verse 1, then to Coda)
Is the wa - ter warm? Is your ma - ma home with you so hap - py?
Sing your lit - tle song; Sing for all your friends. We like to hear you.
With to - mor-row's sun, an-o - ther day's be - gun, You'll soon be wak - ing.
G7
C7
B♭/D
D♯°
C7
Coda
Make hands a pillow and pretend to sleep
Gm7
C9
Gm7
C9
F
C7
C7/F F

Bahay Kubo
(My Nipa Hut)

PUPIL'S PAGE 382

ri. Sing - ka - mas at ta - long, si - ga -
tall. There are tur-nips, there are pea-nuts, there are
G D7 G D
ril - yas at ma - ni, si - tao, ba -
beans all in a row. So man - y
C G C
tao pa - ta - ni.
plants that I grow.
1, 2
D7 G
3
ni.
G Am/G G

Ban Dal
(Half Moon)

ga gi do jal da gan da sɔ jok na ɾa ɾo
With - out a sail or rud - der, tra - vel - ing through the sky.
F
C
F
C
F

Banyan Tree

PUPIL'S PAGE 321

Jamaican Folk Song
Piano Accompaniment by Dean Crocker

you da rock so, un-der ban - yan tree.
D
E7
A
E7
A
E7
A

Bei Fang Chre
(North Wind Blows)

Big Beautiful Planet

PUPIL'S PAGE 376

Words and Music by Raffi
Piano Accompaniment by Anna Marie Spallina

Verse
1. We can feel the pow - er of the noon - day sun, A blaz - ing ball of fire__ up a - bove.
2. We can feel the spir - it of a blow - ing wind, A might - y source of pow-er in our lives.
F
Gm
C7
Gm
C7
Shin - ing light and warmth e - nough for ev - 'ry - one, A gift to ev - 'ry na - tion from a star.
Of - fer - ing an - oth - er way to fill our needs, Na - ture's gift to help us car - ry on.
F
F
Gm
Sing Refrain after each verse
C7
Gm
C7
Coda
F7
B♭7
C7
F7

Bow, Wow, Wow

PUPIL'S PAGE 264

Mother Goose Rhyme
Piano Accompaniment by Dean Crocker

to Coda
Bm
F♯m
D
A
Bm7
D
GM7
A
D
Coda
G
D/F♯
Bm
Asus
A
G
A/G
D/F♯
Bm
D/A
A7
D

Button, You Must Wander

PUPIL'S PAGE 176

American Singing Game
Piano Accompaniment by Dean Crocker

1., 2.
sharp eyes will find you. But-ton, you must wan - der ev - 'ry - where.
B♭
F
F
Dm7
Am
Gm7
C7
F
3.
F
F
C/E
F

Candle on the Water

PUPIL'S PAGE 296

Words and Music by Al Kasha and Joel Hirschhorn
Piano Accompaniment by Dean Crocker

11
Don't give up, you have some-where to turn.
A cold and friend-less tide has
F(add9)
C2/E
G7sus
G7
B♭(add9)
C(add9)
B♭/C
14
found you.
Don't let the storm-y dark-ness pull you down.
Fsus
F
B♭(add9)
C(add9)
B♭/C
F
Gm7/F
F
17
I'll paint a ray of hope a-round you,
cir-cling in the air,
Am7
D7
C/D
Gsus
G
F/G
Em/G
20
D.S. al Coda
light-ed by a prayer.
Dm/G
F/A
G/B
F/A
G

Coda
Look for me reach - ing out to show, as sure as riv - ers
F(add9) G7/F C2/E F2/A Fm/A♭
flow, I'll nev - er let you go.
C(add9)/G F♯m7(♭5) Dm7/G C(add9) G/C
I'll nev - er let you go. I'll nev - er let you
F/C F/G C(add9) G/C F/C F/G G(add9)
To Coda
go.
C(add9) Dm/C F/C C F/C G/C C(add9)

Caranguejo
(The Crab)

PUPIL'S PAGE 306

12
ré. ¡Pal - ma! pal - ma! pal - ma!
sea. Swish, swish, swish, he swish - es,
sand. Click, click, click, he's click - ing,
B♭ B F7
15
¡Pé Pé Pé, Pé! Ca - ran - gue - jo só é
Down a - mong the fish - es. Oh, a crab is not a
With his side - wise kick - ing. Oh, a crab is not a
F7 B♭ B♭
18
pei - xe na en - chen - te da ma - ré.
fish and yet a fish he seems to be.
fish be-cause no fish can swim on land.
F7 B♭/F F B♭
21
B♭ Gm/F F7 B♭

Check It Out! (It's About Respect)

PUPIL'S PAGE 10

Words and Music by
John Higgins and John Jacobson
Piano Accompaniment by Dean Crocker

Lower hands
Drop hands
Treat 'em with re - spect and they'll be there for me. They can
G7 C7 B7 Em
Thumbs to self
(Optional)
Spin once
count on me in the end. It's a -
A sus4 A D11 D
Step clap
L X R X
Point R hand
L
Point L hand
R
bout re - spect! Check it out! Check it out! It's a -
G Em D sus4 C
Step clap
L X R X
Point R hand L and then move it
1. from L to R at chest level
Point R hand L and then move it
2. from L to R at chest level
bout re - spect! Check it out! It's a - out!
G Em D C D

C
One person holds up the letter, OR spell each letter with your body!
R! There's a rea-son peo-ple treat you like they do. E! Ev-'ry-bod-y take a chance. S! It's so sim-ple, and it all be-gins with you. P! Peo-ple got-ta take a stand. E! E-ven when you think the world is-n't fair. C! Come a-long and check it out!
C7
G7
C7
G7
C7
B7
Em

T! Take a risk, take a ride, take a dare. Take a breath of air and let's
A7
D sus4
Punch
R L
shout, RE - SPECT! Check it out! RE - SPECT! Check it out! It's a -
D
D sus4
Step clap L, R (as before)
Point L, R (as before)
Step clap L, R
bout re - spect! Check it out! Check it out! It's a - bout re - spect! Check it
G
Em
C
Point R hand and move L to R (as before)
(Optional)
Fists to hips
out! It's a - out! Huh!

Chiapanecas
(Ladies of Chiapas)

PUPIL'S PAGE 128

Mexican Folk Song
English Version by MMH
Piano Accompaniment by Dean Crocker

B
Bai - la, mi chi‿a - pa - ne - ca. Bai - la,
Dance, now, my chi‿a - pa - ne - ca. Dance with
G
D
bai - la con gar - bo. Bai - la, sua - ve ra - yo de
grace and en - chant-ment. Dance, now, with the moon— shin - ing
A 7
luz.
bright.
Bai - la,
Dance, now,
D
G
mi chi‿a - pa - ne - ca. Bai - la, bai - la con gar - bo.
my chi‿a - pa - ne - ca. Dance with grace and en - chant-ment.
G
D

to Coda
que en el bai - le rei - na e - res tú, chi a - pa - ne - ca gen -
Dance, my gen - tle one, You will soon be the queen of the
A7
D
A7
til. (clap clap)
D
f
D.S. al Coda
A7
D
A7
Coda
dance! (clap clap)
D
A7
D

Chichipapa
(The Sparrow's Singing School)

PUPIL'S PAGE 22

Music by Ryutaro Hirota
Words by Katsura Shimizu
Arranged by Kyoko Takahashi
Piano Accompaniment by Dean Crocker

Chirri Bim

PUPIL'S PAGE 70

Traditional Yiddish Song
Piano Accompaniment by Dean Crocker

ai chir-ri bir-ri bir-ri, ai chir-ri bir-ri bir-ri, chir-ri bir-ri bim bom bom.
Am
Em
B7
Em
Am
B7
Em

Chíu, chíu, chíu
(Chirp, Chirp, Chirp)

Repeat is written out in Student Book

10
2.
Refrain
tar me a - le - gra el co - ra - zón. Con tus gor - je - os, con tu tri -
sing - ing sets my heart a - glow. Your mer - ry chirp-ing, your roun-de -
F7
B♭
F7
13
nar, des - pier - ta el al - ba, la no - che ya se va. Con tus gor -
lay, You bring the dawn - ing, the shad - ows fade a - way, Your mer - ry
B♭
F7
B♭
16
je - os, con tu tri - nar, des - pier - ta el al - ba, la no - che ya se va.
chirp - ing, your roun - de - la. You bring the dawn - ing, the shad - ows fade a - way.
F7
B♭
E♭
F7
B♭

Columbus Sailed with Three Ships

PUPIL'S PAGE 344

Words and Music by Margaret Campbelle-Holman
Piano Accompaniment by Dean Crocker

Solo
Group
o - ver the o - cean blue. The Ni - ña, (the
C5
B♭
F
Solo
Group
Solo
Ni - ña), the Pin - ta, (the Pin - ta), the San - ta Ma -
F/B♭
F6
To Coda
Group
rí - a (the San - ta Ma - rí - a), sailed the o - cean
Dm7
F/B♭
C
blue.
Dm
B♭M7
C

F
B♭/F
FM7
B♭/F
F
B♭/F
Fmaj9
B♭/F
F2sus
Dm
F2sus
Dm
B♭6/9
G9sus
B♭6/9
G9sus
mp
cresc.
E♭6/9
D7sus/C
D7sus
Gm9/B♭
F9/E♭
C5
ff

D.S. al Coda
Co -
Dm
mf
C
C(add2)
C
Coda
blue.
Dm
mf
B♭M7
Gm7
B♭M7
C5
F2sus
p

Corner Grocery Store

PUPIL'S PAGE 311

American Folk Song
Piano Accompaniment by Dean Crocker

cor - ner gro - cery store. My eyes are dim, I can - not see. I
C7 D♭ E♭ F F B♭ D7/A
mf
p
have not brought my specs with me. I have not brought my
Gm Gm/B♭ G7/B C C/B♭ F/A F F/A B♭ D7/A Gm
1. 2.
specs with me!
F/C C7 F
p
f
mf
G♭ F G♭ F G♭ F
mp
p
pp

Cuckoo, Where Are You?

PUPIL'S PAGE 244

American Singing Game
Words Adapted by MMH
Piano Accompaniment by Dean Crocker

Daisy Chain

PUPIL'S PAGE 255

Dal taro kacha
(Come, Pick the Moon)

PUPIL'S PAGE 98

Music by Tae-Hyun Park
Words by Suk Joong Yoon
English Words by Linda Worsley
Piano Accompaniment by Dean Crocker

Dance Together

PUPIL'S PAGE 264

American Folk Song
Piano Accompaniment by Dean Crocker

Dance, Dance, Dance!

PUPIL'S PAGE 5

Music by Moses Hogan
Words by Ava Hogan-Chapman
Piano Accompaniment by Dean Crocker

v1: Shimmy shoulders (imitate)
Jump L (imitate)
v2: Wave hands overhead and swing hips
Swing hands at waist height and swing hips
Clap 4 times
To Coda
B
L R L R L R L R
1. Wig - gle it, wig - gle it, Jump it, jump it,
2. Swing it high, swing it low,
E♭/F
B♭7sus4
D7(♯5)
v1: Jump R (imitate)
Hand Jive: Pat (twice) Clap (twice)
Slice Slice
v2: Repeat previous 2 measures
Hand Jive: Pat (twice)
Clap (twice)
Hop it, hop it, Bop it, bop it, Move it, move it,
Swing it fast, swing it slow, Move it, move it,
E♭9
E°
F11
v1: Hit fists R over L L over R
Fists overhead and rock hips
v2: Slice Slice
Hit fists R over L L over R
Fists overhead and rock hips
L R L R L R L R
Groove it, groove it, 'Til your bo - dy can't stop mov - in'.
B♭6/9
E♭9
G♭maj7
Fm7
D.S. al Coda
Cm7 Dm7 E♭ F11 E♭9sus4 E♭9
Coda
Hit a funky pose.
B♭(add9)

Doggie, Doggie

PUPIL'S PAGE 59

Singing Game
Piano Accompaniment by Dean Crocker

Donkey, Donkey

PUPIL'S PAGE 256

Old English Rhyme
Music by Margaret Campbelle-Holman
Piano Accompaniment by Dean Crocker

Dumplin's

PUPIL'S PAGE 172

Calypso Song from the West Indies
Piano Accompaniment by Dean Crocker

Friend
Cookie
Friend
"One of my dump - lin's gone." "Don't tell ___ me so!" "One of my dump - lin's
"Two of my dump - lin's gone." "Don't tell ___ me so!" "Two of my dump - lin's
D
A7
D
D
A7
Tempo I (♩ = 100)
1.
2.
gone."
gone."
D
p
D
D
A7
D
f

Eating Lizards

PUPIL'S PAGE 250

Words and Music by Carol Huffman
Piano Accompaniment by Dean Crocker

El burrito enfermo
(The Sick Little Donkey)

PUPIL'S PAGE 180

Latin American Folk Song
Arranged by José-Luis Orozco
English Words by Linda Worsley
Piano Accompaniment by Dean Crocker

2. A mi burro, a mi burro
le duele la garganta,
y el médico le manda
una bufanda blanca,
una bufanda blanca,
una gorrita negra
y mueve las patitas
(tap, tap, tap, tap).

Little donkey, my donkey,
my donkey has a sore throat.
The doctor came and gave him
a white scarf for his sore throat,
a white scarf for his sore throat,
a black cap for his headache.
And now his little hooves go
(tap, tap, tap, tap).

3. A mi burro, a mi burro
ya no le duele nada,
y el médico le manda
trocitos de manzana,
trocitos de manzana,
una bufanda blanca,
una gorrita negra
y mueve las patitas
(tap, tap, tap, tap).

Little donkey, my donkey,
my donkey's feeling better.
The doctor came and gave him
some little bits of apple,
some little bits of apple,
a white scarf for his sore throat,
a black cap for his headache.
And now his little hooves go
(tap, tap, tap, tap).

El palomo y la paloma
(The Doves)

PUPIL'S PAGE 381

Mexican Folk Song
Adapted by José-Luis Orozco
English Words by Linda Worsley
Piano Accompaniment by Dean Crocker

Refrain
lar. El pa - lo - mo‿y la pa - lo - ma los dos fue - ron a bai - lar, y‿el pa -
down." Both of them came fly - ing down to land and dance up-on the ground. Mis - ter
C
C
G 7
lo - mo le de - cí - a yo ya quie - ro des - can - sar. El pa - lo - mo‿y la pa -
Dove soon had to stop; he said, "I'm just too tired to hop." Both of them came fly - ing
C
lo - ma los dos fue - ron a bai - lar, y‿el pa - lo - mo le de - cí - a yo ya
down to land and dance up-on the ground. Mis - ter Dove soon had to stop; he said, "I'm
G 7
1.
2.
quie - ro des - can - sar. sar.
just too tired to hop." hop."
C
C
N.C.

El tren
(The Train)

PUPIL'S PAGE 326

Venezuelan Folk Song
Piano Accompaniment by Larry Moore

13
ra - cas" di - ce‿el tren cuan - do vie - ne de Los Te - ques. Pá Ca -
ra - cas," says the train when it's com - ing from Los Te - ques. To Ca -
go - ing through a tun-nel, it goes ver - y, ver - y slow - ly. Ver - y
cros - ses o - ver brid-ges, it be - gins to go much fast - er. Hur - ry,
F C7 F B♭
17
ra - cas, pá Ca - ra - cas, siem - pre lle - ni - to de gen - te pa - sa‿a
ra - cas, to Ca - ra - cas, al - ways ver - y full of peo - ple, some-times
gent - ly, ver - y slow - ly, so the peo - ple won't be fright-ened. Ver - y
hur - ry, hur - ry, hur - ry, we're ar - riv - ing in Ca - ra - cas! Hur - ry,
Gm F C7 F F B♭
21
1., 2., 3.
ve - ces por un tu - nel y‿o - tras ve - ces por un puen - te. 1."To Ca -
pass - ing through a tun - nel, some-times pass - ing o - ver bridg - es. 2. When it's
gent - ly, ver - y slow - ly, so the peo - ple won't be fright-ened. 3. When it
hur - ry, hur - ry, hur - ry, we're ar - riv - ing in Ca
Gm F F C7 F
25
4.
a - cas!
F C7 F

El zapatero
(The Cobbler)

PUPIL'S PAGE 138

Puerto Rican Folk Song
Piano Accompaniment by Dean Crocker

te - ro, us - ted los com - pon - dra.
cob - bler, then will you mend the hole?
Dm C F Gm7 C7 F F Dm C F
B♭ C F F Dm C F Gm7 C7 C7sus F

En la feria de San Juan
(In the Market of San Juan)

PUPIL'S PAGE 226

Puerto Rican Folk Song
English Version by MMH
Piano Accompaniment by Dean Crocker

1., 2., 3.
4.
Juan.
Juan.
G D7 G C D7 G Em
mp
Am D7 G C D7 G Em Am D7 G
Verse
English: In the mar - ket of San Juan, I bought
my - self a whis - tle,
my - self a drum.
a gui - tar.
a vi - o - lin,
G D7 G
Repeat, adding previous verses each time
Refrain
(whistle the melody) the whis - tle.
Tum, tum, tum, tum, the drum.
ta - ra, ta - ra, ta - ra, the gui - tar.
Lin, lin, lin, the vi - o - lin.
Come with me, come with me, to the
D7 G C/E D7/F♯ G Em/B

mar - ket of San Juan. Come with me, come with me, to the mar - ket of San
Am/C D7 G C/E D7/F♯ G Em/B Am/C D7
1., 2., 3.
Juan.
In the
4.
Juan.
G D7 G G C D7 G Em
Am D7 G C D7 G Em Am D7 G

En nuestra Tierra tan linda
(On Our Beautiful Planet Earth)

PUPIL'S PAGE 114

Latin American Folk Song
Adapted by José-Luis Orozco
English Words by Linda Worsley
Piano Accompaniment by Dean Crocker

2. En nuestra Tierra tan linda
pronto va a soplar el viento
pronto va a soplar el viento
en nuestra Tierra tan linda

3. pronto va a caer la lluvia

4. pronto brillará una estrella

2. Here on our beautiful planet,
soon a fresh wind will blow,
soon a fresh wind will blow,
Here on our beautiful planet.

3. soon a warm rain will fall

4. soon a bright star will glow

Engine, Engine Number Nine

PUPIL'S PAGE 13

Aø9 C7
C9 B9(♯5) B♭13 A9
A♭9 G7
C7 B7 C7
mf
G7 G♭7 G7
C9
mf
G7 Am7 C♯°/B♭ G7/B
En-gine, en-gine, num-ber nine, go-ing down the rail-road line!
C9
Dm11 C/E F2
F/G A♯11 C6
C7 B7 C7
If the train goes off the track, will I get my mon-ey back?
C7 B7 C7
C
mp
pp

Ésta sí que es Nochebuena
(This Is Christmas Eve)

PUPIL'S PAGE 361

Mexican Folk Song
Piano Accompaniment by Dean Crocker

Everybody Has Music Inside

PUPIL'S PAGE 164

Words and Music by Greg Scelsa
Piano Accompaniment by Dean Crocker

4 group peel off to clasp "opera" hands, where marked:
grp1
grp2
grp3
grp4
Wipe both hands like "safe" in baseball
You don't have to be a vir - tu - o - so, it does-n't mat-ter if you
E♭M7
E♭dim
E♭
F7
Dm7
A/D
Dm7
Tilt hands with palms down
L
R
L hand to stomach
R hand to stomach
Plié
Up
Reach R hand to L and R
L
R
sing just "so - so." It's a feel-ing down in - side your soul, so come on,
G7sus
E♭+
G7
Cm7
G/C
Cm7
F7
E♭(add2)
Cm7
Point R hand at audience
Hands behind back, step scuff
L
(SR)
R
(SL)
L
(SR)
R
(SL)
you can do it! Ev - 'ry - bod - y has mu - sic in - side,
F
F7
B♭(add2)
B♭
B♭(add2)
B♭
Hands on hips, rock from waist
L
R
L
R
Hold heart and lean L
so let a song ring out. Just let it come right
Cm7
E♭M7/F
F/C

Lean R
Clasp "opera" hands
Plié
Up
from your heart, that's what it's all a - bout.
E♭M7/F
F/C
F
B♭(add2)
B♭/F
A♭/B♭
A♭/C
B♭7/D
Snap L fingers
Snap R fingers
Pat L leg
Pat R leg
Repeat previous measure 2 times
Mu - sic is the sound of life
E♭M7
E♭dim
E♭M7
D7
Cm(add2)
D7/F♯
Scoop both hands
Pat legs with a triplet
L R L
R
Clap
Reach R hand to audience
reaching out for love.
Ev - 'ry - bod - y has
Gm
GM7
Gm7
C sus
C
Cm7(♭5)
B♭M7
B♭6
Clap 3 times
Reach L hand to audience
Clap 2 times
mu - sic,
Ev - 'ry - bod - y has
mu - sic,
Cm7
E♭M7
F
B♭(add2)
Dm7
Gm7
Cm7
Cm7(♭5)

Point R hand to audience
Pat legs with a triplet
L R L R
3
Clap 2 times
Ev - 'ry - bod - y has mu - sic in - side.
B♭M7
B♭6
Cm7
F
B♭(add2)
B♭
Reach R hand to
audience with body facing L
1.
2.
F7sus
F
B♭(add2)
B♭
F7sus
F
F7sus
F
B♭(add2)

Everything Grows

PUPIL'S PAGE 204

Music by Raffi
Words by Raffi and D. Pike
Piano Accompaniment by Dean Crocker

*Verse 2 is written out in Piano Accompaniment

Verse
Hold stomach
Ev - 'ry-thing grows.
2. Food on the farm,
E7
A
Hands together and move them like a fish
fish in the sea,
Flap elbows like wings
Birds in the air,
Wiggle both jazz hands by face
leaves on the
D
A
Rock as before
L R L R
Bend knees
Straighten up
tree. Ev-'ry-thing grows, an - y - one knows that's how it goes.
B7
E
Refrain
Ev-'ry-thing grows and grows.
Ba - bies do, an - i - mals
E7 A/E E7
A
D

too. Ev-'ry-thing grows. Ev-'ry-thing grows and grows.
A
E
D A E
Sis-ters do, bro-thers too. Ev-'ry-thing grows.
E
E7
A sus/D
A/C♯
A sus/B
E7sus
A (add2)

The Food Song

PUPIL'S PAGE 318

Words and Music by Jackie Silberg
Piano Accompaniment by Dean Crocker

12
egg rolls, french fries, ru - ma - ki, Sal - ly Lunn.
Gm
C7
F
E♭7
15
Brat - wurst, la - sa - gna, won ton, chow mein, ce - vi - che,
D7
Gm
G/B
C7
18
1.
2.
crab ran - goon. crab ran - goon.
F
C7
G
A7(♯5)
F
C7
F
C7
Gm
A7
Dm

Four White Horses

PUPIL'S PAGE 301

Caribbean Folk Song
Collected by Lois Choksy
Piano Accompaniment by Dean Crocker

ripe ba - nan - a, Up to - mor - row is a rain - y day.
E C♯m A/B B7/A E D Bm7 E
1.
2.
E D B7 D Bm7 E

Garden Song

PUPIL'S PAGE 236

Words and Music by David Mallett
Piano Accompaniment by Kryste Andrews

Slowly stand up, like a plant growing
Stretch hands way above your head
row by row,__ Some - one bless the seeds I sow,
sun and rain,__ Find my way in na - ture's chain,
hun - gri - ly__ From his perch in yon - der tree.
B♭ F B♭/C C7 F
Gently wave your hands
L R L R
"Rain hands" lower to sides
Some-one warm them from be - low__ 'til the rain comes tum - bl - ing
Tune my bod - y and my brain__ to the mu - sic from__ the
In my gar - den I'm as free__ as that feath - ered thief__ up
B♭ C7 F Dm Gm C7
down.
land.
there.
F B♭ C7 F Dm Gm C7 F

Going Over the Sea

PUPIL'S PAGE 216

Canadian Street Rhyme
Piano Accompaniment by Kay Evans

Refrain
sail - or - man's ship, And the sail - or - man said to me, "Go - ing
Am/C
D7
G
o - ver, go - ing un - der, Stand at at - ten - tion like a
G
1.–9.
sol - dier, With a one, two, and three." 2.–10. When
G
C/G
G
10.
three."
G
G
Am/C
D7
G

Good Night, Sleep Tight

PUPIL'S PAGE 76

Traditional
Piano Accompaniment by Larry Moore

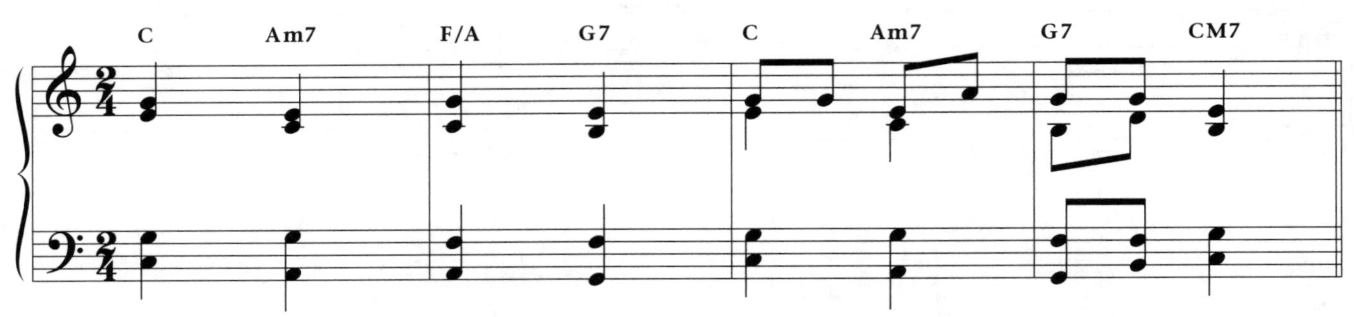

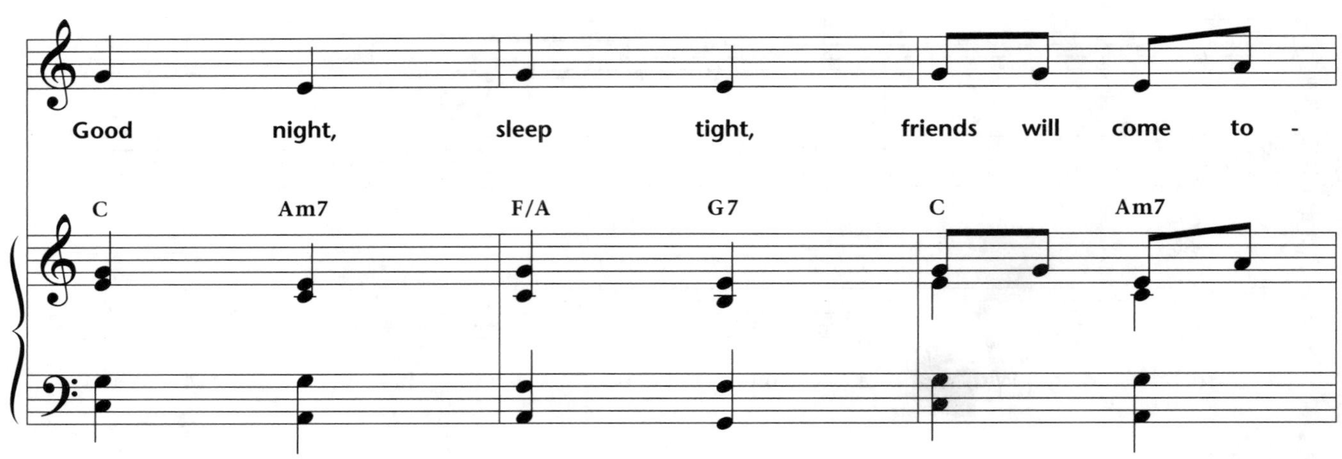

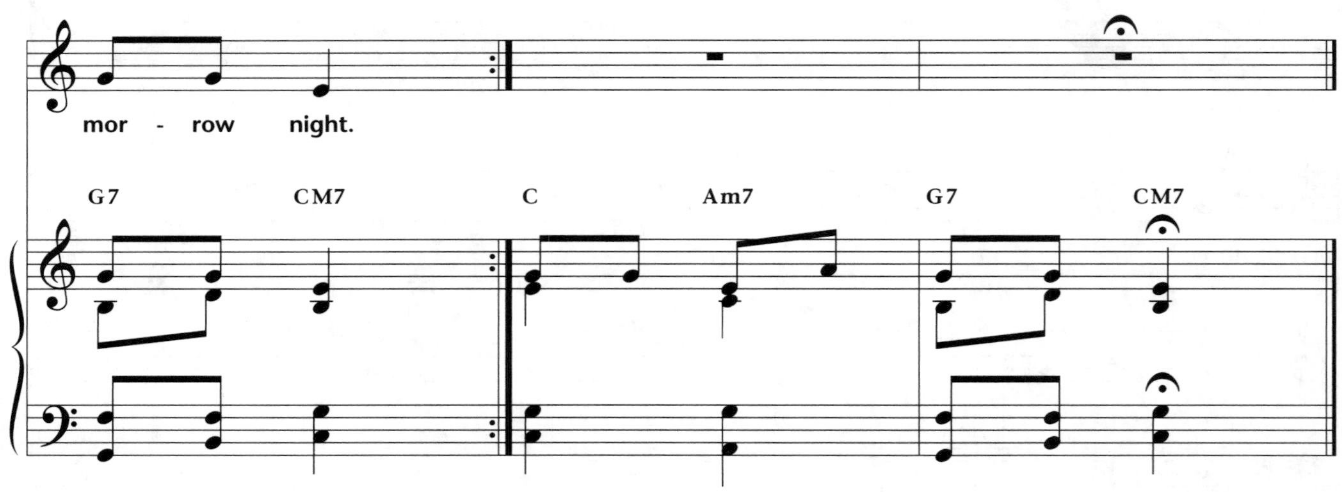

The Great Outdoors

PUPIL'S PAGE 290

Words and Music by George Wilkins
Piano Accompaniment by Dean Crocker

C F G

mp *f*

5

If ya just been wish-in' 'bout go - in' fish - in' and you're

C C

mf

9

still on the shore, grab your camp - in' gear and

F C

12

meet us right here, got all kinds a fun in store. It's

D7 G7

15
time for a va - ca - tion, for some rest and re - lax - a - tion. For -
F
F
C
Am
19
get your cares 'n' join us bears in the great out - doors.
F
G
F
G7
C
23
Ain't noth-in' like the great out - doors to ease your soul.
C7
F
C
27
Ain't noth - in' like the great out - doors to keep you from grow - in' old.
F
C/E
D7

31
—
If your mind's been haz - y and you're feel - in' la - zy 'n'
G7
C
C
34
down on all fours, then join us bears and suck up some air in the
F
C
B♭
F
G
38
1.
great out - doors.
Ain't
F
G7
C
C7
41
2.
doors.
C
G7
C

Green Eggs and Ham

PUPIL'S PAGE 284

Music by Stephen Flaherty
Lyrics by Lynn Ahrens
Piano Accompaniment by Dean Crocker

Point L
Point R
Point 5 times, each time in a different direction
13
do not like them here or there. I do not like them an - y - where. Not
A♭7(♯9) A♭7/C D♭7 Ddim A♭7(♯9) A♭7/F Fdim E♭7 A♭6
Group 2 divides into 4 groups
Each bends forward and shakes head "no" with hands on hips, as marked
grp1
grp2
grp3
grp4
All remain bent forward and shaking heads
17
in a house. Not with a mouse. Not here or there. Not an - y - where. I
D♭ Ddim A♭/E♭ A♭7 D♭ Ddim A♭/E♭ A♭7
All stand up
Wag R fingers
Group 1 (focus at Group 2) hands out, palms up, pulse shoulders
21
do not like green eggs and ham! I do not like them, Sam-I - Am! Could
D♭7 Ddim A♭/E♭ Fm7(♭5) B♭7(♭9) A♭ D

grp1 grp2 grp3 grp4

33

with a goat. Not on a boat. Not in the rain. Not on a train. Not

D D♯dim A/E A7 D D♯dim A/E A7

All remain bent forward shaking heads
All stand up
Group 1, hands out, palms up, lean in
in a house. Not with a mouse. Oh, no! Not
D D♯dim A/E A7 B7(♭5)/F E7 A/E
Group 2 shake head "no"
Group 1 lean in with hands up and out
Group 2 shake head "no"
All
in a box. Not with a fox. Not in a tree. You let me be! I
E♭ Edim B♭7/F B♭7 E♭ Edim B♭7/F B♭7
All jog to C forming one group
All shake heads "no," wag R index finger, as marked
do not like green eggs and ham! I do not like them Sam-I-Am!
E♭7 Edim B♭/F G♭7 Gm7(♭5) Gm G♭7 B♭

Hakuna Matata

PUPIL'S PAGE 292

Music by Elton John
Lyrics by Tim Rice
Piano Accompaniment by Dean Crocker

17
wor-ries
for the rest of your days.
It's our
Cm
E♭/G
A♭
F7/A
F
21
prob-lem - free
phi - los - o - phy.
Ha - ku - na ma-
E♭/B♭
B♭
25
D.S. al Coda
ta - ta.
E♭
D♭
A♭
E♭
D♭2/F
Coda
30
It means no wor - ries
for the rest of your
B♭7/D
G7/B
Cm
E♭/G
A♭

33
days.
It's our prob-lem - free
phi -
F7/A
E♭/B♭
E♭
37
los - o - phy.
Ha - ku - na ma - ta - ta.
B♭7
B♭7/F
E♭
E♭/G
41
Ha - ku - na ma - ta - ta.
A♭
B♭
E♭
45
Ha - ku - na ma - ta - ta.
A♭
B♭7
E♭

Harvest

PUPIL'S PAGE 342

Georgia Folk Song
Piano Accompaniment by Dean Crocker

He's Got the Whole World in His Hands

PUPIL'S PAGE 116

Traditional Spiritual
Piano Accompaniment by Dean Crocker

"Wind" - wave jazz hands
"Rain" - wiggle fingers high to low
"All-State"
"Sun" - clap burst
"Moon" - hands together over head to make a circle
2. He's got the wind and the rain__ in His hands.__ He's got the sun and the moon__
EbM7 Fm7/Bb EbM7 Fm7 Gbdim Eb/G Fm7 Bb9
mp
"All-State"
Wind" - wave jazz hands
"Rain" - wiggle fingers high to low
"All-State"
Burst hands high to low
"All-State"
in His hands.__He's got the wind and the rain__ in His hands.__ He's got the whole world in His hands.__
EbM7 Bb13 EbM7 Fm9 Gbdim Eb/G Fm11 Bb9
Point on "you"
Thumbs to self on "me"
"All-State"
3. He's got you and me, broth-er, in His hands.__ He's got
EbM7 Fm7 F#dim Bb7 Eb/G AbM7 Adim Eb/Bb
mf
Point on "you"
Thumbs to self on "me"
"All-State"
Point on "you"
Thumbs to self on "me"
you and me, sis-ter, in His hands.__ He's got you and me, broth-er,
Fm7 Bb7 Eb/G Ab Bb7sus Bb7 EbM7 AbM7

"All-State"
Burst hands high to low
"All-State"
in His hands. He's got the whole world in His hands.
G7(♯9)
C9
Fm11
E♭/G
A♭/B♭
E♭/G
Fm7
Double-time (♩= 216)
Clap hands double time and step side to side on off beat
E♭7(♯9)
A♭9
E♭7(♯9)
f
1.
A♭9
Fm7
E♭/G
A♭M7
A dim
A♭/B♭
B♭
E♭
2.
B♭7(♯5 ♯9)
A♭/B♭
B♭
E♭

Heigh Ho, Here We Go

PUPIL'S PAGE 252

American Folk Song
Piano Accompaniment by Dean Crocker

Hello, Hello There

PUPIL'S PAGE 126

Music by Jule Styne
Words by Betty Comden and Adolph Green
Piano Accompaniment by Dean Crocker

B
Group 1
Well, well, what do you know?
Dm9
D♭9(♭5)
Cmaj9
A7(♭9)
Group 2
We should have done this a long time a -
Dm7
G7(♭9)
C
Dm7
D♯dim
Group 1
go! Well, well, is - n't it
C/E
Dm9
D♭9(♭5)
Cmaj9
Group 2
swell! Is - n't it nice to say:
A7(♭9)
Dm7
G7

*D.C. al Fine in Student Book is written out in Piano Accompaniment

Here Comes a Bluebird

PUPIL'S PAGE 263

day.
Takes him - self a part - ner, hops in the
F
gar - den, Hey, did - dle - um - a day, day,
F
C7
F
day.
F
F
C7
F

Here Comes Sally

PUPIL'S PAGE 220

African American Folk Song
Piano Accompaniment by Dean Crocker

Com-ing down the al - ley all night long.
Here comes an - oth-er one, all night long.
D
A
D
D
G 7
D
G 7
E 7/G♯
A 7(♯5)
D
rit.

Hey, Hey, Look at Me

PUPIL'S PAGE 245

American Singing Game
Words Adapted by MMH
Piano Accompaniment by Larry Moore

Hop, Old Squirrel

PUPIL'S PAGE 258

Virginia Folk Song
Piano Accompaniment by Ian Williams

Horton Hears a Who!

PUPIL'S PAGE 279

Horton Hears a Who! Two

PUPIL'S PAGE 280

Music by Stephen Flaherty
Lyrics by Lynn Ahrens
Piano Accompaniment by Dean Crocker

Hot Cross Buns

PUPIL'S PAGE 258

English Street Cry
Piano Accompaniment by Larry Moore

I Bought Me a Cat

PUPIL'S PAGE 14

Kentucky Mountain Folk song
Piano Accompaniment by Dean Crocker

hen pleased me. I fed my hen un - der yon - der tree.
duck pleased me. I fed my duck un - der yon - der tree.
goose pleased me. I fed my goose un - der yon - der tree.
pig pleased me. I fed my pig un - der yon - der tree.
cow pleased me. I fed my cow un - der yon - der tree.
horse pleased me. I fed my horse un - der yon - der tree.
F F/G C C Am C/E G7 C
1.
Hen goes chim - my chuck, chim - my chuck. Cat goes fid - dle - i - fee.
Am G Am G C FM7 G C
fz
f
2.
Duck goes quack, quack. Hen goes chim - my chuck, chim - my chuck.
Am(maj 7) Am G/B Am G/B
Cat goes fid - dle - i - fee.
3.
Goose goes
FM7 G C
fz
f

honk, honk. Duck goes quack, quack. Hen goes
C7/A
E5/E♭
chim - my chuck, chim - my chuck. Cat goes fid - dle - i - fee.
Am G Am G FM7 G C
fz
f
4.
Pig goes grif - fy, grif - fy. Goose goes honk, honk.
C7/A
sf
Duck goes quack, quack. Hen goes chim - my chuck, chim - my chuck.
E5/E♭
Am G Am G

5.
Cat goes fid - dle - i - fee. Cow goes moo,
FM7 G C
C+
fz
f
moo. Pig goes grif - fy, grif - fy. Goose goes honk,
C7/A
sf
honk. Duck goes quack, quack. Hen goes
E5/E♭
sf
chim - my chuck, chim - my chuck. Cat goes fid - dle - i - fee.
Am G Am G FM7 G C
fz
f

6.
Horse goes neigh, neigh. Cow goes moo, moo. Pig goes
grif - fy, grif - fy. Goose goes honk, honk. Duck goes
quack, quack. Hen goes chim - my chuck, chim - my chuck.
Cat goes fid - dle - i - fee.
CM7
C+
C7/A
E5/E♭
Am
G
Am
G
Am/C
FM7
G
C
G
C
Am
FM7
G
C
sf
sf
fz
ff

I Chih Ching Wa
(Frogs)

PUPIL'S PAGE 186

Chinese Folk Song
English Words by Linda Worsley
Piano Accompaniment by Dean Crocker

si__ gʊ__ tong kwai dʌ tsau
Have a hap-py bath, Mis-ter Frog!
Bm
Em
F#m
Bm
Em
F#m
Em
F#m
Bm

I Saw Three Ships

PUPIL'S PAGE 359

English Carol
Piano Accompaniment by Larry Moore

3.
morn - ing.
D7 G D Em/D D D7 G/D
D Em/D D G/D D
4.
morn - ing.
D7 G
G D7 Em G/D C G/D
rit.
C D9 G
rit.

I See

PUPIL'S PAGE 266

American Folk Song
Piano Accompaniment by Dean Crocker

I'm Gonna Sing

PUPIL'S PAGE 9

African American Spiritual
Piano Accompaniment by Dean Crocker

1., 2.
3.
bey the spir - it of the Lord.
Lord. And o -
G/D D7 G C6 Am7 G C6
bey the spir - it of the Lord. And o - bey the spir - it of the
G/D D7 G C6 G/D D7
(Optional) rit.
Lord.
A - men.
G
C9
Glissando
rit.
G
Glissando

In and Out

PUPIL'S PAGE 245

American Folk Song
Piano Accompaniment by Larry Moore

In the Window

PUPIL'S PAGE 352

Hebrew Folk Song
English Words by Judith Eisenstein
Piano Accompaniment by Dean Crocker

1., 2., 3.
4.
D
D7
Gm
D7sus
Gm
Dm
5.
6.
D7sus
D7
D7sus
7.
Gm/D
Dm
8.
Gm
C
Cm
Dm
Gm
rit.

Itik Besenda Gurau

(The Ducks)

PUPIL'S PAGE 100

hat ka mu. Kwek! Kwek! Kwek, kwek, kwek! Ber sa ma ra mai.
in a row. Quack! Quack! Quack, quack, quack! Hap - py, hear them say:
A D
Kwek! Kwek! Kwek, kwek, kwek! Me nu ju su ngai! Kwek!
Quack! Quack! Quack, quack, quack! "Let's go swim to - day, Quack!"
D
A7
D
1.
2.
D

It's a Small World

PUPIL'S PAGE 298

Words and Music by
Richard M. Sherman and Robert B. Sherman
Piano Accompaniment by Dean Crocker

17
much that we share, that it's time we're a - ware, it's a
A♭maj 7
A♭7
D♭6
D♭m6
21
small world af - ter all.
A♭/E♭
B♭m/E♭
A♭/E♭
E♭7
A♭
E♭7
Refrain
25
It's a small world af - ter all.
A♭
E♭7
f
29
It's a small world af - ter all.
A♭

33
It's a small world af - ter all. It's a
D♭
D♭m6
37
Verse
small, small world. It's a
A♭/E♭
E♭7
A♭
E♭7
mf
41
world of laugh - ter, a world of tears; it's a
A♭
A♭/C
C♭dim
B♭m7
E♭7
45
world of hopes and a world of fears. There's so
B♭m7
E♭7
A♭dim
A♭

49
much that we share, that it's time we're a - ware, it's a
D♭
D♭m
53
small world af - ter all.
A♭/E♭
B♭m/E♭
A♭/E♭
E♭7
A♭
E♭7
Refrain
(Spanish) Not found in pupil's edition
57
Muy pe - que - ño‿el mun - do es.
A♭
E♭7
3
3
61
Muy pe - que - ño‿el mun - do es.
E♭7
A♭
3
3

65
De-be ha - ber más her - man - dad muy pe -
A♭7
D♭
D♭m6
69
que - ño es. It's a
A♭/E♭
E♭7
A♭
E♭7
mp
73
world of laugh - ter, a world of tears; it's a
A♭(add9)
A♭
A♭(add9)
A♭
D♭/A♭
E♭7
E♭7
A♭/E♭
77
world of hopes and a world of fears. There's so
D♭/A♭
E♭7
D♭/A♭
E♭7
A♭(add9)
A♭/E♭
A♭(add9)
D♭/A♭

81
much that we share, that it's time we're a - ware, it's a
A♭
A♭7
D♭
D♭m6
85
small world af - ter all.
A♭/E♭
E♭sus/D♭
A♭/C
E♭7/B♭
A♭
E♭7
(Japanese) Not found in pupil's edition
89
Se - ka - i wa se - ma - i
N.C.
93
Se - ka - i wa - o - na - ji

97
Se - ka - i wa ma - ru - i Ta - da
hi - to - tsu. It's a small,
A♭/E♭
E♭7
Fm7
B♭9
A♭/E♭
f
small world.
E♭7
A♭
D♭
D♭m/E♭
A♭
A♭6 9
A♭
ff

It's Possible

PUPIL'S PAGE 281

Music by Stephan Flaherty
Lyrics by Lynn Ahrens
Piano Accompaniment by Dean Crocker

All look around nodding
to each other in agreement
pos - si - ble.
An - y-thing's pos - si - ble!
G6/9
Gmaj9
G6/9
R index finger points out
R hand moves up
to shield eyes
All circle
bodies around
It might go a - long down where no one can see, right
G
D
G/D
D
Point R index finger twice,
as marked
R arms
"swim" back
L arms
"swim" back
X
X
un - der State High - way Two - Hundred - and - Three! Right un - der the wag - ons! Right
D
Bm7
A
D
D
R arms
"swim" forward
L arms
"swim" forward
All focus on "Kid 5"
Kid 5
All
Bounce body
R
L
un - der the toes of Mis - sus Um - bro - so who's hang - ing out clothes! It's
G/D
D
D
Bm7
A
Bm7

All look around nodding to each other in agreement
pos-si - ble. An - y - thing's pos - si - ble! This
G6/9 Gmaj7 Em/D D
All retrieve paper fish cutouts
might be a riv - er, now might-n't it be, con - nec-ting Mc - El - li - got's pool
G(add9) D/F♯
All present their fish, pulsing it 3 times, as marked
with the sea! Then may - be some fish might be swim - ming, swim - ming toward me!
Bm7 G(add9) G/B A D/E
All swim their fish in excitement
Oh, the
A D G C/G G

sea is so full_ of a num-ber of fish. If a fel-low is pa - tient, he might get his wish! And
D G/D D D Bm7 A A/C♯D
that's why I think_ that I'm not such a fool when I sit here and fish in Mc - El - li-got's Pool. It's
Speed fish up
D G/D D D Bm7 A Bm7
Stop Slow fish Stop Speed fish up
pos-si - ble._ An - y-thing's pos - si - ble!_ It's
G D/G Em/D D
Stop
Pulse fish towards audience
twice, as marked
X X
pos-si - ble._ An - y - thing's pos - si - ble!_
Em/D G(add9) G G6 D/A G6/D D

It's Raining! It's Pouring!

PUPIL'S PAGE 233

Anonymous
Piano Accompaniment by Dean Crocker

Ja posejah lubenice
(I Planted Watermelons)

Refrain
17
Hay_ and straw,_ hay_ and straw,_ Oats, oats, oats, oats, oats, oats.
Gm F E♭ Dm C
21
B♭ F B♭

Jim Along, Josie

PUPIL'S PAGE 194

American Folk Song
Piano Accompaniment by William N. Simon

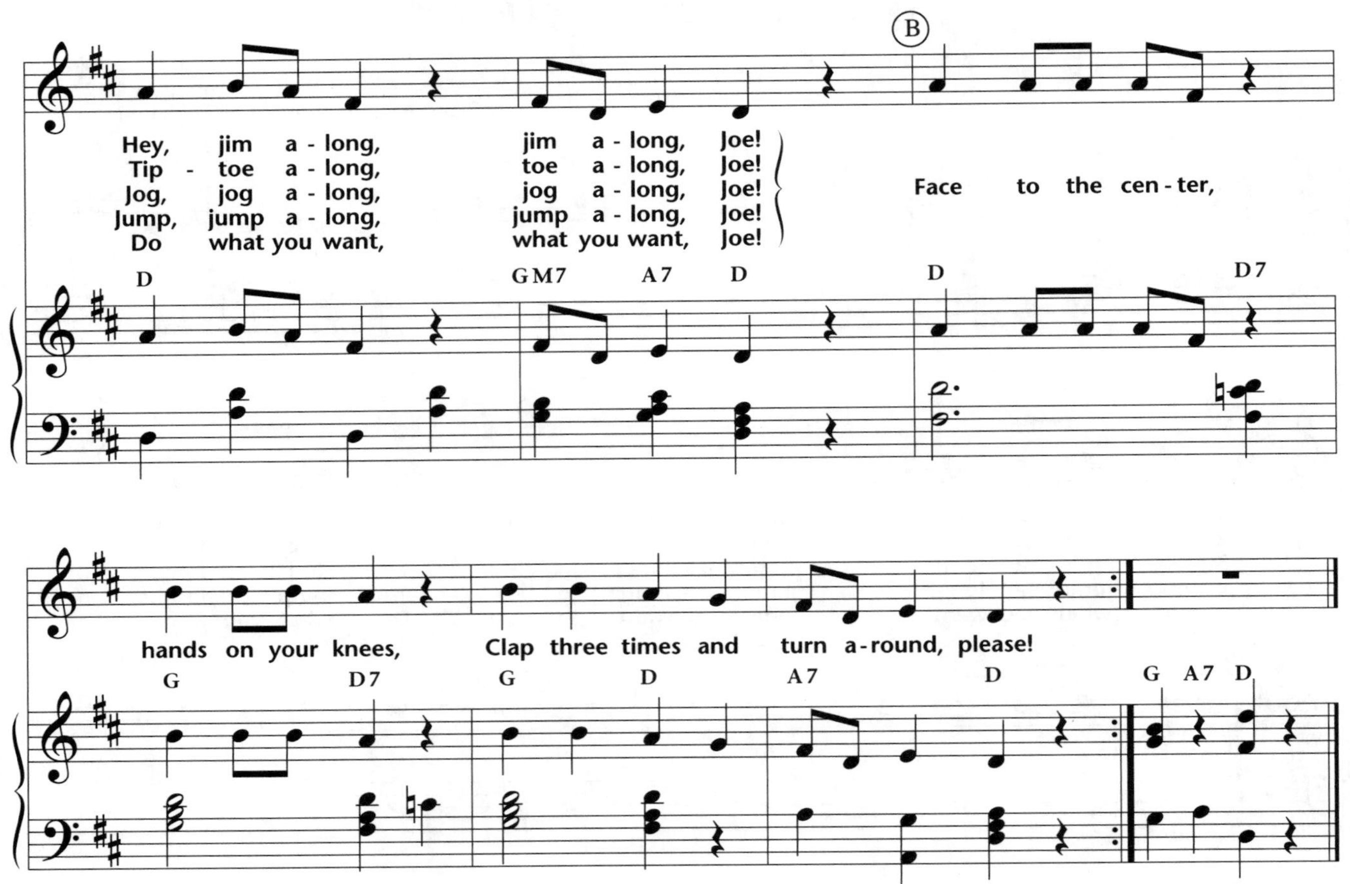
B
Hey, jim a - long, jim a - long, Joe!
Tip - toe a - long, toe a - long, Joe!
Jog, jog a - long, jog a - long, Joe!
Jump, jump a - long, jump a - long, Joe!
Do what you want, what you want, Joe!
Face to the cen - ter,
D GM7 A7 D D D7
hands on your knees, Clap three times and turn a-round, please!
G D7 G D A7 D G A7 D

Joy

PUPIL'S PAGE 46

Words and Music by Hap Palmer
Piano Accompaniment by Dean Crocker

Pop Gospel (♩ = 126)

F F♯dim C/G G♯dim Am7 Dm7 C/E F F/G C

f

1., 3. Joy, I feel the joy of mu - sic.
2. *(2nd time instrumental)*

C F/C C G7 Dm7 G7

mf

Joy, I feel the joy of rhy - thm, and my

G7 Dm7 G7 F/G C F/C C E7

heart it starts sing - ing. And my bod - y starts sway - ing

F C

ev - 'ry - time I feel the joy of mu - sic.
G7 Dm7 G7 G13 C F/C C
F C/E F F♯dim FM7/G F/G C F/G C

Juan Pirulero

PUPIL'S PAGE 270

Folk Song from New Mexico
Piano Accompaniment by Dean Crocker

Jugaremos en el bosque
(We Will Play in the Forest)

PUPIL'S PAGE 188

Collected and Transcribed by Carol J. Brown
English Words by Linda Worsley
Piano Accompaniment by Dean Crocker

1.–4.
Wolf answers:
¿Lo - bo, lo - bi - to‿es - tás a - llí?
Wolf, won't you tell us, are you there?
1. Me estoy bañando.
I'm taking a bath.
2. Me estoy secando.
I'm drying off.
3. Me estoy peinando.
I'm combing my hair.
4. Me estoy poniendo los tenis.
I'm putting on my tennis shoes.
5.
Wolf answers:
¿Lo - bo, lo - bi - to‿es - tás a - llí?
Wolf, won't you tell us, are you there?
5. ¡Alli voy!
I'm coming!
Gm
Adim
D7
Gm

King's Land

PUPIL'S PAGE 257

American Folk Song
Piano Accompaniment by Dean Crocker

I'm on the king's land, the king is not at home. He's gone to Bos - ton, to
D G D F♯m Bm D G A sus A D G D F♯m Bm
mf
buy his wife a comb.
A sus A D B♭/D C/G A D
ff

Knock the Cymbals

PUPIL'S PAGE 265

Traditional Play-Party Song
Piano Accompaniment by Dean Crocker

3. Right hand crossed, do, oh do, Right hand crossed, do, oh do, Right hand crossed,
do, oh do, Oh-law, Su-sie gal.
4. Pro-me-nade a-round, do, oh do,
Pro-me-nade a-round, do, oh do, Pro-me-nade a-round, do, oh do, Oh-law, Su-sie
gal.
F Dm F F Dm C F Dm
F Am B♭ Csus C6 F F Dm/C F
F Dm/C C F Dm/C F Am B♭ Csus C6
F Csus F F Gm7 Csus F

La bella hortelana
(The Beautiful Gardener)

PUPIL'S PAGE 208

Traditional Mexican Song
English Words by Linda Worsley
Piano Accompaniment by Dean Crocker

2. Cuando riega . . .
3. Cuando corta . . .
4. Cuando muele . . .
5. Cuando come . . .

2. When she goes watering
3. When she goes reaping
4. When she is grinding
5. When she is eating

Land of the Silver Birch

PUPIL'S PAGE 88

Canadian Folk Song
Piano Accompaniment by Dean Crocker

Refrain
Boom de de boom boom, Boom de de boom boom, Boom de de boom boom, Boom.
B♭(add9)
C(add9)
B♭maj7
C(add9)
Dm
B♭(add9)
mf
p
1.
2.
Gm
F/E♭
A sus
A
F/E♭
Dm(add9)

Leatherwing Bat

PUPIL'S PAGE 304

Appalachian Folk Song
Piano Accompaniment by Dean Crocker

Refrain
How - did-dle-dow - dee did-dle-um - day, How - dee - dow - dee
Em D Em
did-dle - um day. Dee-how - dee - dow - dee-did-dle-um - day. And - a -
G D Em C
hey - dee - lee - lee - lye - dee - low.
Em Em/D B7sus B7 Em Am
C Am B7sus B7 Em

Lemonade

PUPIL'S PAGE 19

American Singing Game
Piano Accompaniment by Dean Crocker

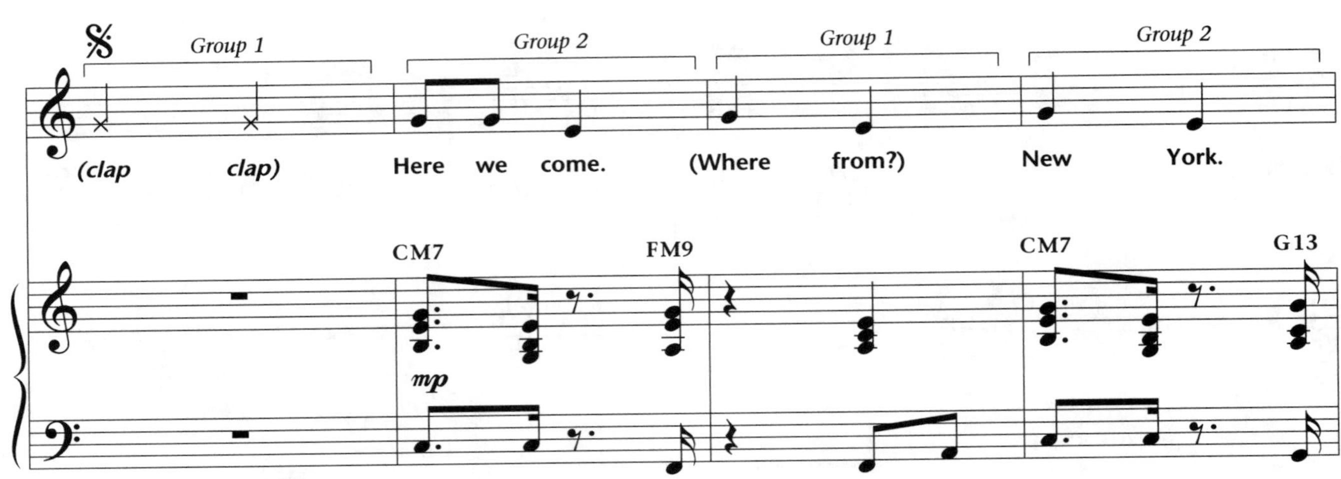

Group 1
To Coda
(Get to work and make us some.)
Dm7 C/E FM7 G13 CM7 CM7 FM9
f
mf
CM7 G13 CM7 FM9
D.S. al Coda
Em7 Am7 Dm7 C/E FM7 G13 CM7
Coda
CM7 FM9 CM7 G13
f

Let's Go Fly a Kite

PUPIL'S PAGE 134

Words and Music by Richard M. Sherman
and Robert B. Sherman
Piano Accompaniment by Steve Hoover

Refrain
kite.
kite.
Oh!
Oh!
Let's go
C
C7/E
F
mf
fly a kite, Up to the high - est height!
C
Let's go fly a kite, And send it
G
Dm
soar - ing, Up through the at - mos - phere,
D♯dim
C/E
F

Up where the air is clear. Oh, let's
C
G7
go fly a kite!
1.
2. When you
C
mp
G7
2.
kite!
C
C
C

Little Sally Water

PUPIL'S PAGE 249

African American Folk Song
Piano Accompaniment by Dean Crocker

Zydeco (♩ = 104)

D

mf

Lit - tle Sal - ly

D

Wa - ter, sit - ting in a sau - cer, Rise Sal - ly, rise Sal - ly,

D

wipe a - way your tears, Sal - ly. Turn to the east, Sal - ly, Turn to the

D

west, Sal - ly. Turn to the one that you love the best, Sal - ly.

1.
D
D
2.
D

Mama Paquita

PUPIL'S PAGE 92

Brazilian Carnival Song
English Version by Merrill Staton
Piano Accompaniment by Bill and Pat Medley

Shrug L
Shrug R
Can't buy pa - pa - yas, can't buy ba - nan - as;
Can't buy pa - ja - mas, can't buy som - bre - ros;
G7
L hand down
Right hand down
She can - not buy pa - pa - yas or ba - nan - as.
She can - not buy pa - ja - mas or som - bre - ros.
G7
Wag R index finger
Tilt claps
L
No, ma - ma - ma - ma, Ma - ma Pa - qui - ta,
No, ma - ma - ma - ma, Ma - ma Pa - qui - ta,
C
G7
C
R
L
R
Ma - ma Pa - qui - ta, Ma - ma Pa -
Ma - ma Pa - qui - ta, Ma - ma Pa -

Shrug
Hold face in hands "Home Alone"
qui - ta will not have a ripe pa - pa - ya; No ripe pa -
qui - ta will not have the fine pa - ja - mas; No fine pa -
C
G7
Shrug L
Shrug R
pa - ya, no ripe ba - nan - a, So go to
ja - mas, no fine som - bre - ros, So go to
G7
Tilt Claps
L
R
Present both hands high
1.
Car - ni-val to laugh and dance and sing.
Car - ni-val to laugh and dance and
G7
C
A7
Present both hands high
2.
2. Ma - ma Pa - sing.
Dm7
G7
C

Martin Luther King

PUPIL'S PAGE 364

Words and Music by Mary Donnelly
Arranged by George L.O. Strid
Piano Accompaniment by Dean Crocker

1.
He was a man who died for free-dom. Mar-tin Lu-ther King.
He taught us how to make a dif-'rence. Mar-tin Lu-ther King.
C C/B Am Fm(maj7) C/G Dm/G C F/G
2.
Ev'-ry-bod-y sing! Mar-tin Lu-ther King!
C Dm/C C
Mar-tin Lu-ther King! Sing, Mar-tin Lu-ther,
C/E E♭dim Dm11 F/G C Dm7 Dm11
cresc.
Mar-tin Lu-ther, Mar-tin Lu-ther King!
C/E F F♯dim C/G F/G C F/C C
f

Mary Had a Baby

PUPIL'S PAGE 360

African American Spiritual
Piano Accompaniment by Dean Crocker

What did Ma-ry name him? Yes, my Lord, What did Ma-ry name him? Yes, Lord, The
F Gm/F FM7 Gm/C F Gm Am B♭ Am7 A♭dim
peo-ple keep a-com-ing and the train has gone.
Gm7 F/A B♭M7 F/C Gm/B♭ F/A Gm7 F Gm7 Am Gm
3. Ma-ry named him Je-sus, Yes, Lord, Ma-ry named him Je-sus, Yes, my Lord,
F Gm Am B♭ C F Gm Am B♭ C
mf
Ma-ry named him Je-sus, Yes, Lord, The peo-ple keep a-com-ing and the
F Gm Am B♭ C F/A Dm/A B♭M7

train has gone. 4. Where was Je - sus born?_ Yes, Lord,
F/C Gm/B♭ F/A Gm F Gm Am B♭ C F Gm/F Am/F Gm/F
Where was Je - sus born?__ Yes, my Lord, Where was Je - sus born?_ Yes, Lord, The
F Gm/F Am/F Gm/F F C/E B♭/D C
peo - ple keep a - com - ing and the train has gone.
F/C B♭/D F/C Gm/B♭ F/A Gm F Gm7 F/A Gm
5. Born in low - ly sta - ble, Yes, Lord, Born in low - ly sta - ble, Yes, my Lord,
F Gm Am B♭ C F Gm Am B♭ C
f

Born in low-ly sta - ble, Yes, Lord, The peo - ple keep a com - ing and the train has gone.
F Gm Am B♭ C F/A B♭M7 F/C B♭ F/A Gm
6. Where did Ma - ry lay him? Yes, Lord,
F F/A B♭ Am Gm7 F Gm/F Am/F Gm/F
p
Where did Ma - ry lay him? Yes, my Lord. Where did Ma - ry lay him? Yes, Lord, The
F Gm/F Am/F Gm/F F Gm Am B♭ Am A♭dim
peo - ple keep a - com - ing and the train has gone.
Gm7 F/A B♭M7 F/A Gm/B♭ F/A Gm7 F Gm F/A B♭9 B♭/D C

7. Laid him in a man - ger, Yes, Lord, Laid him in a man - ger, Yes, my Lord,
F Gm/B♭ Am/C B♭ C F Gm/B♭ Am/C B♭ C
Laid him in a man - ger, Yes, Lord, The peo-ple keep a-com-ing and the train has gone.
F Gm/B♭ Am/C B♭ C F B♭ F Gm/C F
F/A Gm/B♭ Am/C B♭/D C Gm7/F F

Matarile

PUPIL'S PAGE 261

Mexican Folk Song
Piano Accompaniment by Dean Crocker

English:
1. What do you want? Ma - ta - ri - le, ri - le,
2. What do you want? Ma - ta - ri - le, ri - le,
3. What do you want? Ma - ta - ri - le, ri - le,
D
A7
ri - le. I want to jump, Ma - ta -
ri - le. I want to march, Ma - ta -
ri - le. I want to run, Ma - ta -
D
D
ri - le, ri - le, ron.
ri - le, ri - le, ron.
ri - le, ri - le, ron.
A7
D
D
A7
D

Me gase boho
(Orange Tree)

PUPIL'S PAGE 317

Sinhala Folk Song
English Version by Mary Lu Walker
Piano Accompaniment by Dean Crocker

Me Stone

PUPIL'S PAGE 48

Folk Song from Trinidad and Tobago
Piano Accompaniment by Dean Crocker

Mein Hut
(My Hat)

1.
2.
ist er nicht mein Hut. My hat. Mein
would not be my
G7 C C G7
3.
Hut.
C C F/C C G7 G7 Am7 G7/B C
mp
ff

Merry-Go-Round

PUPIL'S PAGE 267

Music by Marilyn Copeland Davidson
Words by Dorothy Baruch
Piano Accompaniment by Dean Crocker

'Round and 'round and up and down, I sat high up on a
C C♯dim Dm C Em A7
accel.
big brown horse And rode a - round on the mer - ry - go - round And
Dm7 G9 C A7/C♯ Csus/D G9
rode a - round on the mer - ry - go - round. I rode a - round on the
C Gm/B♭ Am7 A♭maj7 C/G F/G
rit.
mer - ry - go - round, A - round and 'round and 'round.
C/G A7/G Dm9 G7 C

The Mill Song

PUPIL'S PAGE 52

American Singing School Song
Piano Accompaniment by Dean Crocker

Mister Rabbit, Mister Rabbit

Ev' - ry lit - tle soul must shine, shine, shine.
F
Dm
B♭
C
F
C7
F
Dm
F
C
F
F
Dm
B♭
C
F

Mother, Mother

PUPIL'S PAGE 254

American Jump Rope Game
Piano Accompaniment by Dean Crocker

1., 2., 3.
G
D
E7
A7
4.
G
D
G
D
D
D7/C
G7/B
Em7(♭5)
A7
D
D6/9
pp

Mouse, Mousie

PUPIL'S PAGE 254

Hungarian Folk Song
Piano Accompaniment by Dean Crocker

Mr. Frog

PUPIL'S PAGE 257

American Singing Game
Piano Accompaniment by Dean Crocker

My Dreidel

PUPIL'S PAGE 353

Music by S.E. Goldfarb
Words by S.S. Grossman
Piano Accompaniment by Dean Crocker

Cm/G
G7
Cm
G/D
G
Cm

Na belo
(Little Heron)

Oh, the Thinks You Can Think!

PUPIL'S PAGE 276

Music by Stephen Flaherty
Lyrics by Lynn Ahrens
Piano Accompaniment by Dean Crocker

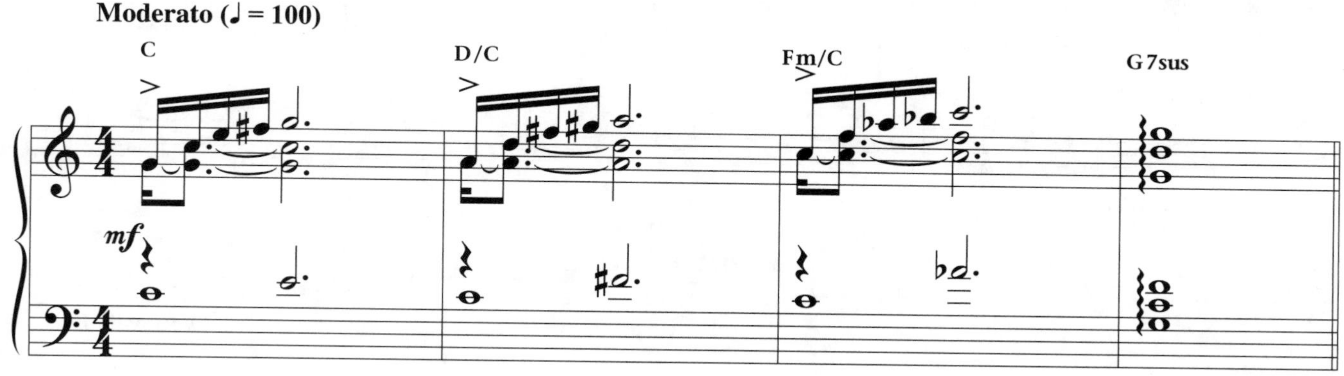

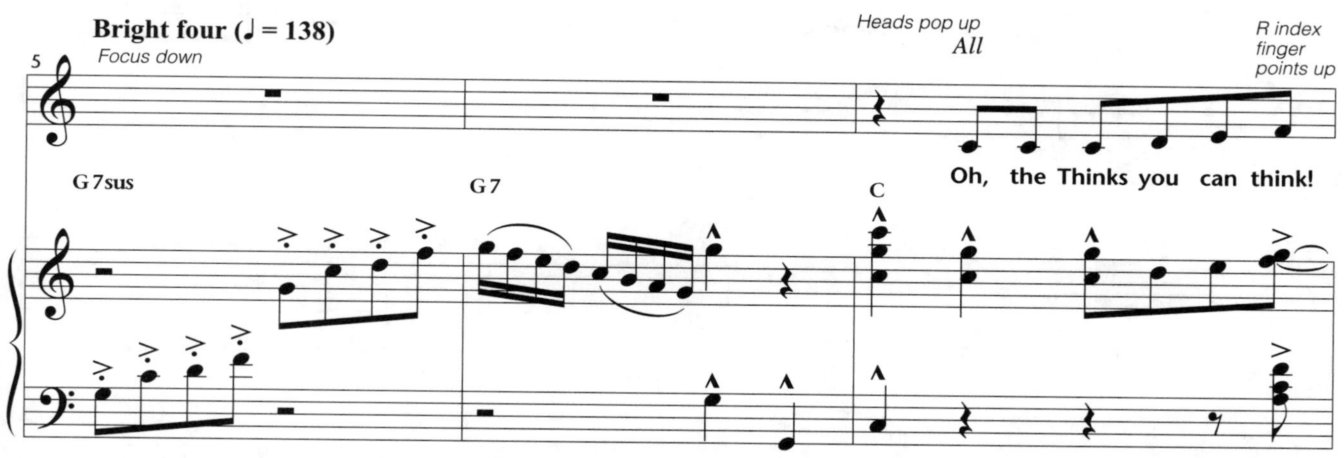

Strike a "reading" pose
Strike a "stinky" pose
In 3 groups break pose and focus to audience, as marked
grp1
Think in - vis - i - ble ink! Or a Gink with a stink! Or a stair to the sky!
C
F(add2)
Gsus
All slap knees
Hands raise over heads
Hands "sunburst" down
grp2
grp3
If you o - pen your mind, oh, the Thinks you will find
C
G
Am
Em
C7
Wiggle body
Heads pop up, focus on audience
R index finger points up
lin - ing up to get loose... Oh, the Thinks you can think
F
D7
Ddim
C/G
R index finger points to head and melts down
All take 2 steps forward and strike a final "thinking" pose
(Optional)
when you think a - bout Seuss! Seuss!
G7sus
C
F
F/G
Csus/G
C
sffz

Old Blue

PUPIL'S PAGE 213

name was Blue, I had a dog and his
hol - low tree, Chased that pos-sum up a
hol - low tree, Caught that pos-sum up a
good and brown, Baked that pos - sum
A7 D D
name was Blue, and I bet - cha five dol - lars he's a
hol - low tree, Best hunt-in' dog you
hol - low tree, Best hunt-in' dog you
good and brown, Laid sweet po - ta - ters
D Gmaj7
good dog, too. Here, Blue, you good dog, you.
ev-er did see. Here, Blue, you good dog, you.
ev-er did see. Here, Blue, you good dog, you.
all a - round. Here, Blue, you good dog, you.
A7 D D Bm A7 D
D Bm A7 D

Old Woman and the Pig

PUPIL'S PAGE 130

Oliver Twist

PUPIL'S PAGE 268

American Folk Song
Piano Accompaniment by Anna Marie Spallina

Oma Rapeti
(Run, Rabbit)

O - ma ra - pe - ti, o - ma ra - pe - ti, o - ma o - ma o - ma!
A7
D
English: Run, rab - bit, run, rab - bit, run, run,
D
A
run! Don't give the far - mer his
A
fun, fun, fun. He'll get
D
D

by with - out his rab - bit pie, so
A
run, rab - bit, run, rab - bit, run, run,
A7
D
1.
run!
A
2.
run!
D6
D

On Top of Spaghetti

PUPIL'S PAGE 312

ta - ble And on - to the floor,
tast - y As tast - y could be,
ghet - ti All cov - ered with cheese,
F
C
And then my poor meat - ball Rolled out of the
And ear - ly next sum - mer, It grew in - to a
Hold on to your meat - balls And don't ev - er
C
G
G7
1., 2.
3.
door. 2. It rolled in the
tree. 3. The tree was all
sneeze.
C
G7
C7
C
A - choo!
F
G7(♭9)
C

Pairs or Pears

PUPIL'S PAGE 265

English Rhyme
Piano Accompaniment by Dean Crocker

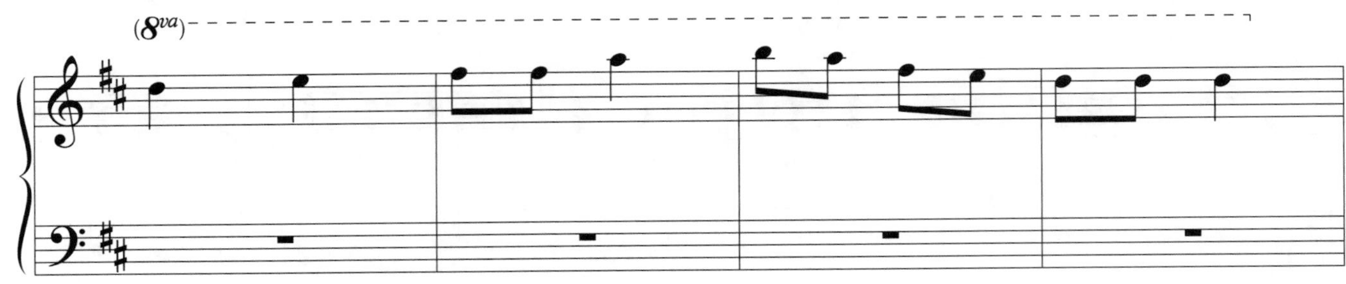

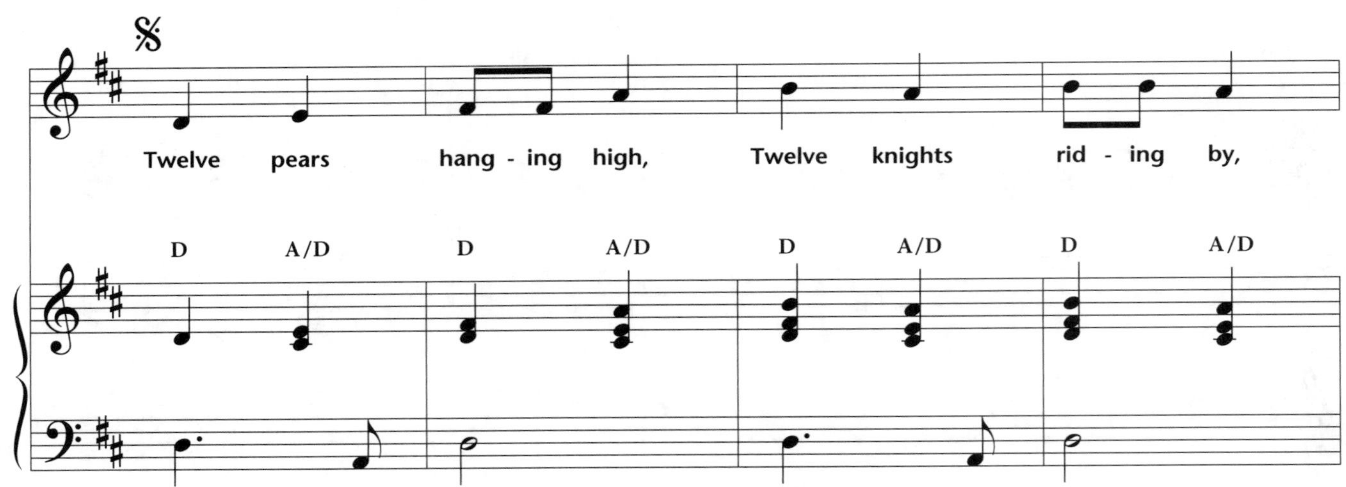

To Coda
Each knight took a pear, And yet left a doz - en there.
D
A/D
D
A/D
D
A/D
D
D
A/D
D
A/D
D
A/D
D
A/D
D.S. al Coda
D
A/D
D
A/D
D
A/D
D
Coda
8va

Part of Your World
from the movie *The Little Mermaid*

PUPIL'S PAGE 294

Music by Alan Menken
Words by Howard Ashman
Piano Accompaniment by Dean Crocker

1.
2.
feet.
street.
Csus
C
Dm7
C7/E
C
Up where they
walk,
up where they
run,
up where they
stay
all
day
in
the
F
F7/E♭
B♭/D
sun.
Wan - der - in'
free,
wish I could
be
part
of
that
B♭m/D♭
F/C
B♭2/D
C7
1.
2.
world.
Up where they
world.
F
B♭/F
C
Dm

Out of the sea,
wish I could be
part of that
world.
B♭m/D♭
Gm7(♭5)/D♭
F/C
B♭/C
C
p
B♭/F
C/F
B♭/F
C/F
F

A Pat on the Back

PUPIL'S PAGE 74

American Folk Song
Piano Accompaniment by Dean Crocker

D.S. al Coda
No - bod - y knows what's apt to hap-pen to - mor - row. So
F
C
G

Coda
day.
C
C7
F
F/A
C
G7
C

Pick a Pumpkin

PUPIL'S PAGE 347

Words and Music by Naomi Caldwell
Piano Accompaniment by Larry Moore

Then we'll be read - y for Hal - low - een! Hal - low - een,
F C F C/G G C F C
Hal - low - een, Then we'll be read - y for Hal - low - een!
F C F C F C/G G C
Hal - low - een, Hal - low - een, Then we'll be read - y for
F C F C F C F
Hal - low - een!
C/G G C F C F C/G G C

Pizza, Pizza, Daddy-O

PUPIL'S PAGE 62

African American Singing Game
Piano Accompaniment by Dean Crocker

Group
Leader
Group
Swim it, swim it, dad - dy - o, Let's duck it! Duck it, duck it, dad - dy -
D
Leader
Group
Leader
Group
o, Let's twist it! Twist it, twist it, dad-dy - o, Let's end it! End it, end it, dad-dy-
D
1., 2.
o!
D7
F
D7
F
(Optional)
3.
Piz-za, piz - za, dad-dy - o,
Piz-za, piz - za, dad-dy - o.
D
F
D7
F
D7
Tag

A Place in the Choir

PUPIL'S PAGE 308

Words and Music by Bill Staines
Piano Accompaniment by Dean Crocker

15
one on the bot - tom where the bull - frog___ croaks, and the
take up the mid - dle, while the hon - ey - bee___ hums and the
lit - tle birds___ sing___ On the mel - o - dies with the
sing - in' in the day___ The lit - tle duck___ quacks, then he's
F
C7
17
hip - po - pot - a - mus moans and groans with a
crick - et fid - dles, The don - key brays and the
high notes ring - ing. The hoot owl hol - lers o - ver
on his way.___ The 'pos - sum ain't got___
F
B♭
19
big to - do, And the old cow just goes
po - ny neighs, and the old coy - o - te___
ev - 'ry - thing And the jay - bird dis - a -
much to say And the por - cu - pine talks to him -
F
C7
21
1., 3.
2., 4.
Refrain
moo. The howls. All God's crit-ters got a place in the choir,
grees. self.
F
F
E
F
Gm/F
F

25
Some sing low, Some sing high-er, some sing out loud on the tel-e-phone wire, And
C7
F
B♭
G7/B
F/C
Dm7
29
some just clap their hands or paws or an-y-thing they got now.
Gm11
C7
F
F sus/B♭
F
B♭/C
F
32
3. It's a sim-ple song of liv-ing sung ev-'ry-where_ By the ox and the fox and the
F
C7
35
griz-zly bear,_ The grump-y al-li-ga-tor and the hawk a-bove, The
F
B♭
F

38
sly rac - coon and the dove. All God's crit-ters got a place in the choir,
C7 F E F F Gm/F F
42
Some sing low, Some sing high-er, some sing out loud on the tel - e - phone wire, And
C7 F B♭ G♯dim F/C
46
some just clap their hands or paws or an - y - thing they got now.
Gm11 C7 F F sus/B♭ F B♭/C F F
50
B♭ F C B♭ C F

Plainsies, Clapsies

PUPIL'S PAGE 248

American Folk Song
Piano Accompaniment by Dean Crocker

D.S. al Coda
D G D G A D
Coda
D Em D/F♯ G A D

Puff, the Magic Dragon

PUPIL'S PAGE 54

Words and Music by Peter Yarrow and Leonard Lipton
Piano Accompaniment by Steve Hoover

land called Hon - ah - lee. Lit - tle Jack - ie
Puff's gi - gan - tic tail. No - ble kings and
way for oth - er toys. One gray night it
long the cher - ry lane, With - out his life - long
C7
F7
B♭
Pa - per loved that ras - cal Puff, and
prin - ces would bow when - 'er they came.
hap - pened Jackie Pa - per came no more, And
friend, Puff could not be brave, So
Dm
E♭
B♭
brought him strings and seal - ing wax and oth - er fan - cy
Pir - ate ships would low'r their flags when Puff roared out his
Puff, that migh - ty dra - gon, he ceased his fear - less
Puff, that migh - ty dra - gon sadly slipped in - to his
E♭
B♭
F/A
Gm
C7
F7

Refrain
stuff. Oh!
name. Oh!
roar. Oh!
cave. Oh!
Puff, the mag - ic drag - on,
lived by the sea And frol - icked in the
au - tumn mist in a land called Hon - ah - lee.
Puff, the mag - ic drag - on, lived by the
B♭ F7 B♭ Dm
E♭ B♭ E♭
B♭ F/A Gm C7 F7
B♭ Dm E♭

sea And frol - icked in the au - tumn mist in a
B♭
E♭
B♭
F/A
Gm
1., 2., 3.
4.
land called Hon - ah - lee.
2. To
3. A
4. His
land called
C7
F7
B♭
C7
Hon - ah - lee.
F7
B♭
B♭
Dm
E♭
F
B♭

Red Rover

PUPIL'S PAGE 249

American Singing Game
Piano Accompaniment by Dean Crocker

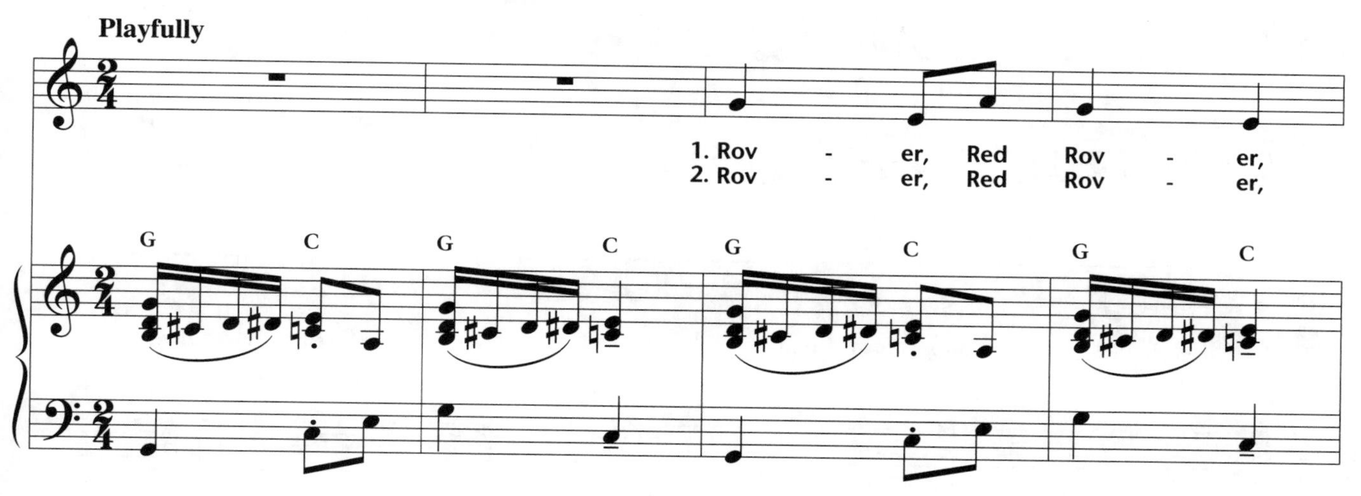

Riddle Song

PUPIL'S PAGE 251

Marilyn Copeland Davidson
Piano Accompaniment by Dean Crocker

few - er there will be.
when a - way I've flown.
G7sus4
G
C
F
F# dim
G
G7
C
G7
C

Riqui Ran
(Sawing Song)

Rover

PUPIL'S PAGE 260

1. I have a dog and his name is Ro - ver. He is the one I love the best.
2. When he is good, he is good all o - ver. When he is bad, he is just a pest.
D A7 D A7 D A7 D
Em7 A13 D D D/F♯ G E7/G♯ Em11 A9 A7 D

Sailor, Sailor on the Sea

PUPIL'S PAGE 262

Words and Music by Jean Ritchie
Piano Accompaniment by Dean Crocker

on the sea, What trea - sures have you brought for me?
on the land, I've gold and jew - els in my hand.
Bm Bm/A Em/G D/A A7 G/D D
3. You have guessed the num - ber true. You have guessed the
D A/D D A7 D/A A7
num - ber true. You have guessed the num - ber true, Now
D D A/C♯ Bm Bm/A
you may sail the o - cean blue. 4. You have missed the
Em/G D/A A7 G G(add9)/A D A7/D
f

num - ber plain. You have missed the num - ber plain.
D
A7
D/A
A7
D
You have missed the num - ber plain, So I must sail the
D
A7/C♯
Bm
Bm/A
Em/G
D/A
A7
sea a - gain.
G/D
D
D(add9)
Bm9
mf
D(add9)
A(add9)
D

Sally Go 'Round the Sun

PUPIL'S PAGE 268

Nursery Rhyme
Piano Accompaniment by Kay Evans

Sammy Sackett

PUPIL'S PAGE 146

American Folk Song
Piano Accompaniment by Dean Crocker

San Serení

PUPIL'S PAGE 323

Latin American Folk Song
Piano Accompaniment by Dean Crocker

San Se - re -

C G7 C C

6

ní de la bue - na, bue - na vi - da, ha - cen a - sí, a -

G7 G7

11

1.–5.

sí { los za - pa - te - ros, / las bai - la - do - ras / los car - pin - te - ros / las pi - a - nis - tas / los cam - pa - ñe - ros / las cos - tu - re - ras } a - sí, a - sí, a - sí, a - sí me gus-ta a mí!

C C G7 C

17
6.
mí!
C
G7
C

Say Your Name

PUPIL'S PAGE 243

Words by Sue Snyder
Music by Marilyn Copeland Davidson
Piano Accompaniment by Dean Crocker

Seeds and Seasons

PUPIL'S PAGE 206

Words and Music by Jim Walters
Piano Accompaniment by Dean Crocker

thun - der is heard on the plain, Ev - 'ry
time for the seed - ling to grow. Ti - ny
up for the heat and the light. Through the
har - dy and strong in the sun, Us - ing
bees find the nec - tar they need, Nev - er
seed will fall in - to the ground. It will
Bm A G/A A D A
seed that in win - ter was sleep - ing Will a -
roots will reach down to the wa - ter, Tak - ing
stem it will lift up the wa - ter, So the
nut - ri - ents, sun - light, and wa - ter, To make
know - ing they car - ry the pol - len, So the
sleep in the mea - dow all win - ter, To a -
D A G D D7
Refrain
wak - en and swell in the rain. And the
life from the warm earth be - low.
leaves will grow stur - dy and bright.
food un - til sum - mer is done.
blos - som can make a new seed.
wake when the spring comes a - round.
G D/F♯ Em 7 A D

sea - son will cir - cle, will cir - cle a - round, And the sea - son will cir - cle a -
G D/F♯ Em 7 D Bm GM7 A
1.–5.
round.
2. And the
3. Then a
4. And the
5. In the
6. Then at
D
6.
round.
G D/F♯ Em 7 D Bm GM7 A D

Seussical Mega-Mix

PUPIL'S PAGE 287

Music by Stephen Flaherty
Lyrics by Lynn Ahrens
Piano Accompaniment by Dean Crocker

The choreographed movements used in the "Seussical Mega-Mix" are like those in the first appearance of the song. For reference, use the Grade-Level DVD.

All slap knees
grp3
Hands raise over heads
Hands "sunburst" down
Wiggle body
If you o-pen your mind, oh, the Thinks you will find lin-ing up to get loose...
Am
Em
C7
F
Heads pop up, focus on audience
R index finger points up
Oh, the Thinks you can think when you think a-bout
D7
Ddim
C/G
G7sus
Gently (♩. = 48)
R index finger points to head and melts down
Slowly sit
In 5 groups slowly stand and focus on Horton, as marked
grp1
Seuss!
I'll just have to
F/C G/D Am/E Csus/F
Bm
grp2
grp3
save him be-cause, af-ter all, a per-son's a per-son, no
G/C
D
Em
Gsus/A
G/B
poco a poco rallentando

Gentle sway
grp4
grp5
R
L
R
rit.
mat - ter how small. A per - son's a per - son, no mat - ter how
B7/D♯
Em
Am7(add11)
G/B
D7sus
rit.
Moderate two-feel (♩ = 148)
Stop, focus out to audience
Cast retrieves paper cutout fish
The fish swim
small.
Oh, and
mp
ff
that's why I think that I'm not such a fool When I sit here and fish in Mc -
D
G/D
D
D
Bm7
El - li - got's Pool. It's pos - si - ble. An - y - thing's
Stop
Slower
A
Bm7
Em/D
G(add9)
G
f

Pulse fish towards audience, as marked
Bright swing (♩= 188)
Put fish away
pos - si - ble!
G6 D/A G6/D D A♭
Group 2, hands on waist, bend forward, shake head "no"
I do not like green eggs and ham. I
E♭11 A♭7(♯9) A♭7/C D♭7 Ddim
do not like them Sam - I - Am. I do not like them
A♭7(♯9)/E♭ A♭7/F B♭7(♭9) B♭7(♭5) E♭11 A♭7(♯9) A♭7/C
Point L Point R Point 5 times, each time in a different direction
here or there. I do not like them an - y - where. Not
D♭7 Ddim A♭7(♯9) A♭7/F Fdim E♭7 A♭6

Group 2 divides into 4 groups
Each bends forward and shakes head "no" with hands on hips, as marked
grp1
grp2
grp3
in a house. Not with a mouse. Not here or there. Not
Db
Ddim
Ab/Eb
Ab7
grp4
All jog to C forming one group
All shake heads "no," wag R index finger, as marked
an - y - where. I do not like green eggs and ham! I do not like them,
Db7
Fm7(b5)
Bb7(b9)
Freestyle
Pose up
Sam - I - Am!
Seuss!
Shake head "no," as marked
Wag R index finger, as marked
Seuss! I do not like green eggs and ham.
Fb9
Eb9
Ab6

Shake the Papaya Down

PUPIL'S PAGE 90

Calypso Song
Collected by W. S. Haynie
Piano Accompaniment by Dean Crocker

D.S. al Coda
F
B♭6
C7
B♭
C7
F
C
Coda
F
B♭6
C7
Gm7
C7
B♭
C7
F

She'll Be Comin' 'Round the Mountain

PUPIL'S PAGE 33

Hoedown! (♩= 112)

Southern Mountain Song
Piano Accompaniment by Dean Crocker

G(add9) CM7 D G(add9) CM7 C/D G/C D7(no3rd) E♭ F E♭

f

1. She'll be com - in' 'round the moun-tain when she comes, *(toot)* *(toot)* She'll be

D G(add9) C/G G /D G Am7(♭5) G/B C/D

mf

com - in' 'round the moun-tain when she comes, *(toot)* *(toot)* She'll be com - in' 'round the

G(add9) Am9 GM7/B C6 D CM7/D D7 G(add9)

moun-tain, She'll be com - in' 'round the moun-tain, She'll be com - in' 'round the moun-tain when she

Am/G G CM7 A7/C♯ G/D CM7 C/D D

comes. (toot) (toot) 2. She'll be driv - ing six white hor - ses when she comes, (whoa
G Cm/E♭ G/D G C/G GM7 E♭
back, toot, toot) She'll be driv - ing six white hor - ses when she comes, (whoa
F Am7(♭5) G/B C/D D G Am9 GM7/B C6 D A♭M7
back, toot, toot) She'll be driv - ing six white hor - ses, She'll be driv - ing six white
F CM7/D D7 G(add9) G(add9)/B C(add9)
hor - ses, She'll be driv - ing six white hor - ses when she comes. (whoa back, toot,
A7/C♯ G(add9)/D CM7 C/D D G E♭ F Cm/E♭

toot) 3. Oh, we'll all go out to meet her when she comes, (hi there, whoa
G/D G(add9) C/G G /D G CM7 E♭
back, toot, toot) Oh, we'll all go out to meet her when she comes, (hi
F Am7(♭5) G/B C/D D G(add9) Am9 GM7/B C D
there, whoa back, toot, toot) Oh, we'll all go out to meet her, Oh, we'll
CM7 A♭M7 F CM7/D D7 G Am/G G
all go out to meet her, Oh, we'll all go out to meet her when she comes. (hi
CM7 A7/C♯ G/D CM7 C/D D G

there, whoa back, toot, toot) 4. Oh, we'll all have chick-en and dump-lings when she
CM7 E♭ F Cm/E♭ G/D N.C.
comes, (yum, yum, hi there, whoa back, toot, toot) Oh, we'll
G/B CM7 E♭ F Am7(♭5) G/B C/D
all have chick-en and dump-lings when she comes, (yum, yum, hi there, whoa
N.C. D D/F♯ CM7 A♭M7
back, toot, toot) Oh, we'll all have chick-en and dump-lings, Oh, we'll all have chick-en and
F CM7/D D7 G G(add9)/B C

dump-lings, Oh, we'll all have chick-en and dump-lings when she comes. (yum, yum, hi
A/C♯ G/D CM7 Am7/D G
there, whoa back, toot, toot) 5. She will have to sleep with Grand-ma when she
CM7 E♭ F Cm/E♭ G/D G G D6/F♯
comes, (snore–in, snore–out, yum, yum, hi there, whoa back, toot,
C/E GM7 CM7 E♭ F Am7(♭5)
toot) She will have to sleep with Grand-ma when she comes, (snore–in, snore–out, yum,
G/B C/D D G D/F♯ C(add9)/E GM7/D C6

yum, hi there, whoa back, toot, toot) She will have to sleep with
D/F♯ CM7 A♭M7 F CM7/D D7 G(add9)
Grand-ma, She will have to sleep with Grand-ma, She will have to sleep with Grand-ma when she
G(add9)/B C(add9) A7/C♯ G(add9)/D CM7 C/D D
comes. (snore–in, snore–out, yum, yum, hi there, whoa back, toot,
G CM7 E♭ F Cm/E♭
toot)
G/D CM7/G D(add9)/F♯ G CM7 D C/D CM7 D7 E♭ F D G

Sheep Shearing

PUPIL'S PAGE 102

Swedish Folk Song
English Words by Sam Blum
Piano Accompaniment by Dean Crocker

Refrain
Surr, surr, surr, surr, surr, surr, Wheel spins a-round, hear, hear the sound;
C7
F
C7
F
mf
Surr, surr, surr, surr, surr, surr, Then we shall dance 'til morn - ing.
C7
F
C7
F
C7
B♭
F
B♭
C7
F

Shoheen Sho

PUPIL'S PAGE 140

Welsh Folk Song
Verse 1 Traditional Welsh Words
Verse 2 and 3 by Margaret Campbell-Holman
Piano Accompaniment by Anthony Brackett

in the nest, Sun doth sink in the West.
C7 G Dsus4 D G Am7 G C6 D7 G

G C6 D6 G

Shoo, Fly

PUPIL'S PAGE 222

American Folk Song
Piano Accompaniment by Ian Williams

A
feel, I feel, I feel, I feel, I feel like a morn - ing star. Oh, Shoo, fly, don't
C7
C7
F
C7
F
both - er me, Shoo, fly, don't both - er me, Shoo, fly, don't both - er me, For
C7
C7
F
F
C7
I be-long to some-bod - y.
C7
F
F
C7(♯9)
C7
F
F
C7
C7
E
F

Shrimp Boats

PUPIL'S PAGE 179

Words and Music by
Paul Howard and Paul Weston
Piano Accompaniment by Dean Crocker

Shrimp boats is a - com - in', there's danc - in' to - night.
F
B♭
F
C9
F
F
B♭
F
C9
F

Sing! Sing! Sing!

PUPIL'S PAGE 196

ev - er I am feel - ing low, I take my smile and go, go, go. Sing, Sing, Sing.
is - n't just a luck - y chance that the peo - ple want to dance. Sing, Sing, Sing.
F
Dm
B♭
C
F
Ne - ver will I be a - fraid, mu - sic I can al - ways make.
Re - mem - ber can and nev - er can't spread your wings and nev - er land.
F
Dm
Refrain
Sing, Sing, Sing. Let's all just sing, make me mu
B♭
C
F
Dm
- sic, make me hap - py. Let's all just
G7
Gm7
Csus4
C
F

1.
sing, make me ma - gic.
Sing, Sing, Sing.
Dm
G7
B♭
C
2.
Sing, Sing, Sing.
2. I'm
F
B♭
C
F

Skating

PUPIL'S PAGE 350

Words and Music by Lynn Freeman Olson
Piano Accompaniment by Dean Crocker

smooth and free. When I am skat - ing I am hap-py as I can
B♭M9 Gm7 E♭M9 E♭/F F7 Gm7 E♭M7 Cm7 E♭/F F7
be!
1.
B♭ E♭/F Gm11
E♭M9 Gm11 E♭M9 E♭/F
2.
Gm7 E♭M9 F9sus4 B♭(add9)

Skinnamarink

PUPIL'S PAGE 368

Tin Pan Alley Song
Piano Accompaniment by Dean Crocker

love you in the eve - ning, 'neath the sil - v'ry moon. Skin - na - ma - rink a - dink a - dink,
C Dm7 C F7 B♭ Gm
skin - na - ma - rink a - doo, I love you.
2nd time to Coda
B♭ Fm G7 C7 F13 B♭
B♭ E♭7 B♭ E♭7 B♭/D C♯dim7
F7/C F7 Cm7 F7 Cm7 F7

Cm7
F7
B♭
B♭
G dim7
B♭/F
B♭
E♭
Gm
E♭/G
C7/G
Gm7
C7/B♭
C7/E
F7
D.S. al Coda
B♭
A7
Fm/A♭
G7
C7
F13
B♭
F7 (♯5)
Coda
you.
B♭
F7 (♯5)/E♭
F7(♭9)
B♭

Step in Time
from the movie *Mary Poppins*

PUPIL'S PAGE 6

Words and Music by Richard M. Sherman
and Robert B. Sherman
Piano Accompaniment by MMH

Flap like a bird - ie, step in time! Nev-er need a rea - son, nev-er need a rhyme,
Step in___ time,___ step in time! Nev-er need a rea - son, nev-er need a rhyme, when you
G
A7
1.
2.
Flap like a bird - ie, step in time! step in time, you
A7
D
A7
step in time.
G
A7
D

Strawberry Roan

PUPIL'S PAGE 66

bronc - bust - ing cow - boy by the looks of your clothes."
throw - ing good rid - ers, the___ horse had good luck.
tried then to throw me right___ up to the skies.
Em A A7
Refrain
Well, it's oh, that straw - ber - ry roan!___
D A7 D
Oh, that straw - ber - ry roan,___ That
G A7 D
straw - ber - ry pon - y no one ev - er rode, And the
G Em A7 D

cow - boy that tries it is sure to get thrown.
G
Em
A7
D
D.C. al Fine after repeat
Oh, that straw - ber - ry roan!
A
A7
G
A
G
A7
D

Take Me Out to the Ball Game

PUPIL'S PAGE 56

Music by Albert von Tilzer
Words by Jack Norworth
Piano Accompaniment by Dean Crocker

back, Let me root, root, root for the home team, If they don't
G7
C
G
C7
win, it's a shame, For it's one, two, three strikes you're
F
F
F♯dim
C/G
2nd time to Coda
out At the old ball game.
A7
D7
G7
C
Gaug
C
D.S. al Coda
Gaug
D♭
A♭aug
C
G7

Coda
game.
C
F
f
F♯dim
C
D7
G
C
G7(♯5)
C

Thank You

PUPIL'S PAGE 349

Music by Franz Schubert
Piano Accompaniment by Dean Crocker

There Are Many Flags In Many Lands

PUPIL'S PAGE 341

Composer Unknown
Words by M.H. Howliston
Piano Accompaniment by MMH

stripes and white stars, too; For there is no flag in an - y land, Like our
D♭
E♭
A♭
D♭
A♭
own Red, White — and — Blue.
D♭
E♭
A♭
E♭
A♭

There's a Hole in the Bucket

PUPIL'S PAGE 132

American Dialogue Song
Traditional German Melody "Liebe Heinrich"
Piano Accompaniment by Dean Crocker

hole, then, dear Geor - gie, dear Geor - gie, dear Geor - gie, Mend the hole, then, dear
knife, dear Geor - gie, dear Geor - gie, dear Geor - gie, With a knife, dear
wet it, dear Geor - gie, dear Geor - gie, dear Geor - gie. Then wet it, dear
G C Am7 C G
Geor - gie, dear Geor - gie, the hole.
Geor - gie, dear Geor - gie, a knife.
Geor - gie, dear Geor - gie then wet it.
3. With
9. The
15. With
C A7 D G Am7 G
p
mp
what shall I mend it, dear Li - za, dear Li - za, With what shall I
knife is too dull, dear Li - za, dear Li - za, The knife is too
what shall I wet it, dear Li - za, dear Li - za. With what shall I
G C Am7/G A7sus/G G

mend it, dear Li - za, with what?
dull, dear Li - za, too dull.
wet it, dear Li - za, with what?
4. With a
10. Then
16. With
C/G
A7
D7
G
mf
mp
straw, dear Geor - gie, dear Geor - gie, dear Geor - gie, With a straw, dear
sharpen it dear Geor - gie, dear Geor - gie, dear Geor - gie. Then sharpen it dear
wa - ter, dear Geor - gie, dear Geor - gie, dear Geor - gie. With wa - ter, dear
G
C
C/E
G
Geor - gie, dear Geor - gie, a straw.
Geor - gie, dear Geor - gie sharpen it.
Geor - gie, dear Geor - gie with water.
5. The
11. With
17. In
C
A7
D
G
C
D7
G
mf
f

straw is too long, dear Li - za, dear Li - za, The straw is too
what shall I sharpen it, dear Li - za, dear Li - za. With what shall I
what shall I get it, dear Li - za, dear Li - za. In what shall I
G C G
p
long, dear Li - za, too long.
sharpen it, dear Li - za, with what?
get it, dear Li - za, in what?
6. Cut the
12. With a
18. In a
C D G C Am7 Am7/E D7
f
straw, dear Geor - gie, dear Geor - gie, dear Geor - gie, Cut the straw, dear
stone, dear Geor - gie, dear Geor - gie, dear Geor - gie. With a stone, dear
buck - et, dear Geor - gie, dear Geor - gie, dear Geor - gie. In a buck - et, dear
G C/G G
mf

Optional: Repeat Verse 1 at end.

This Is Halloween

PUPIL'S PAGE 346

Words and Music by Teresa Jennings
Piano Accompaniment by Dean Crocker

B♭aug Aaug A♭aug Gaug G♭aug Caug A♭aug G C
2.
Boo!
Caug Baug B♭aug Aaug B♭aug Baug Caug D♭aug C Fm

This Is My Country

PUPIL'S PAGE 87

Music by Al Jacobs
Words by Don Raye
Piano Accompaniment by Dean Crocker

All put R hand to heart
I pledge thee my al - le - giance, A - mer - i - ca the
F
C/E
Am7
Dm7
Pat legs
Clap
Pat legs
Salute R hand to chest
Pat legs
Clap
Pat legs
R salute to head
bold, for This is my coun - try, to
G7
A♭7
G7
C
F
G7
Burst R hand from head down
Bring hand to heart
have and to hold!
Am7
Dm7
G7
C
Am7
Dm7
F/G
G
D.S. al Coda
(Optional Interlude)
A♭
Gm7
Fm7
Dm7(♭5)
G
C
Am7
Dm7
G sus
mf

C
Am7
Dm7
G sus
D.S. al Coda
D9
Coda
I pledge thee my al - le - giance, A - mer - i - ca the
FM7
Faug
F6
Em7
C/E
mf
bold, for This is my coun - try, to
G
G♭/A♭
Fm7
B♭/E♭
A♭/D
A♭/G
G7

(optional)
have and to hold! To have
Am7 Dm7 G7 C F C/E Dm7 C/E F F♯m7(♭5)
and to hold!
G sus N.C. C

The Tiki Tiki Tiki Room

PUPIL'S PAGE 324

Words and Music by Richard M. Sherman
and Robert B. Sherman
Piano Accompaniment by Dean Crocker

2nd time to Coda
Ti - ki Room.
Eb
Bb7
Eb
Wel - come to our trop - i - cal hide a - way, you
Eb
mf
Ab6
luck - y peo - ple you! If we were-n't in the show start-ing
Bb7
Eb
right a - way, we'd be in the aud - i-ence too. All to - geth - er!
Ab6
Fm7
Bb7
Eb

Coda
23
The bird of par - a - dise is an el - e - gant bird. It
E♭
A♭6
26
likes to be seen and it loves to be heard. Most lit - tle bird - ies will
B♭7
E♭
29
(D.C. al Fine in Pupil's Edition)
fly a - way, but the Ti - ki Room birds are here ev - 'ry day. In the
A♭6
Fm7
B♭7
E♭
B♭7
f
32
Ti - ki Ti - ki Ti - ki Ti - ki Ti - ki Room, in the Ti - ki Ti - ki Ti - ki Ti - ki
E♭
A♭6
B♭7

35
Ti - ki Room, all the birds sing words and the flow - ers croon in the
E♭
A♭6
Fm7
38
Ti - ki Ti - ki Ti - ki Ti - ki Ti - ki Room.
B♭7
E♭
40
B♭7
E♭
ff

Tinga Layo

PUPIL'S PAGE 50

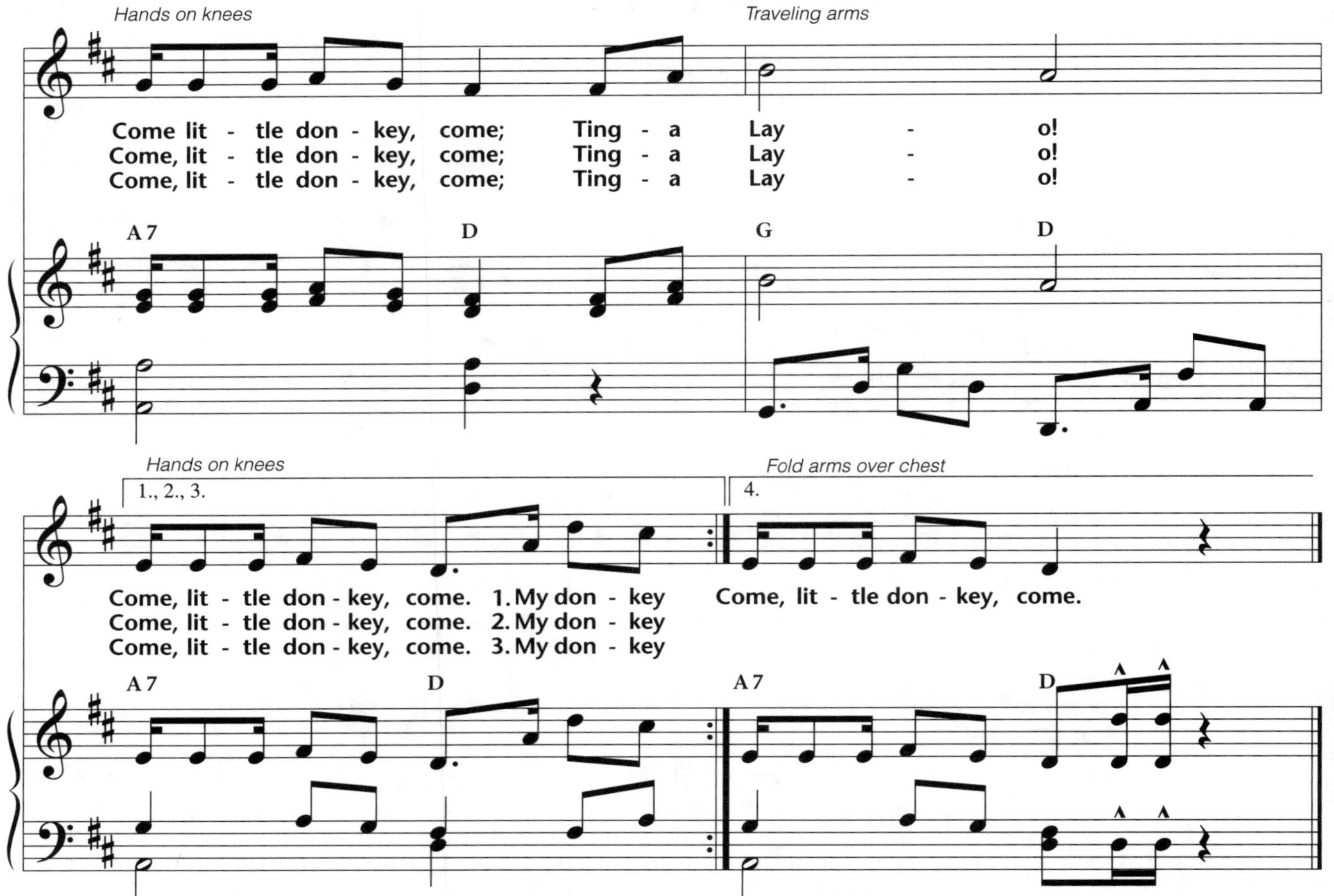
Hands on knees
Traveling arms
Come lit - tle don - key, come; Ting - a Lay - o!
Come, lit - tle don - key, come; Ting - a Lay - o!
Come, lit - tle don - key, come; Ting - a Lay - o!
A 7
D
G
D
Hands on knees
Fold arms over chest
1., 2., 3.
4.
Come, lit - tle don - key, come. 1. My don - key
Come, lit - tle don - key, come. 2. My don - key
Come, lit - tle don - key, come. 3. My don - key
Come, lit - tle don - key, come.
A 7
D
A 7
D

Up on the Housetop

PUPIL'S PAGE 356

B
Refrain
Hold stomach
Shrug
Hold stomach
Shrug
Ho, ho, ho, Who would-n't go? Ho, ho, ho, Who would-n't go?
G
D
A7
D
Point R hand up
Snap finger of both hands 3 times
Point R hand high to low
Fists on hips. Nod 2 times
X X
Up on the house - top, click, click, click, Down through the chim-ney with good Saint Nick.
D
G D G
D
A7 D
A7
A7
D
fz

Wake Up the Sun

PUPIL'S PAGE 124

Words by John Jacobson
Music by Emily Crocker
Piano Accompaniment by Dean Crocker

Look directly at audience
R arm—rainbow arm that ripples across choir
Wake up the sun so the day can come. Put 'way the moon and the
FM7
Gm7
FM9
stars.
Look directly at audience
This is the time now so ev - 'ry - one,
B♭M7/F
E♭M7
Dm7
Am7
B♭M7
v1: Wipe hands in front of eyes
v2: Hands to knees
Verse
come for this day will be ours.
1. Shad - ows will van - ish,
2. She might be shy
Gm7
E♭6/9
C9
B♭/F
F
B♭
C/B♭
v2: Point to self, then to audience
Both vs: Hands to knees
Stand straight slowly
dew dis - ap - pear, the world can be - gin a - new.
like you and I, wait - ing so long to grow.
Am7
Dm7
Gm7
C7sus
C7
Dm7
F/C

Scoop L hand from waist to chest height
Scoop R hand to chest height
1 clap burst
Each day a new start, year af - ter year. Now let the sun shine
She'll hes - i - tate, she'll make us wait. Now's the time to
B♭
C7/B♭
Am7
Dm
Gm7
E♭M9
1.
2.
1 silent/slow clap burst
through, for you! show your glow!
C7sus
C7
C7sus
A♭M7
Slowly look up at "sun"
Some - bo - dy wake the sun.
C11
8va
F(add9)
G7
p
(8va)
G(add9)
F
F(add9)
G7
F

We Wish You a Merry Christmas

PUPIL'S PAGE 358

English Carol
Piano Accompaniment by Dean Crocker

D.S. al Coda
bring us some fig - gy pud - ding, And bring it out here. 3. For
we love our fig - gy pud - ding, So bring some out here. 4. We
won't go un - til we get some, So bring some out here.
B Em G/B C Am D7 G
Coda
Year.
G D7 G D7/F♯ Em Bm Em7 Bm7/D C Am7 D7 G
f
rit.

We're Sailing Down the River

PUPIL'S PAGE 166

American Folk Song
Piano Accompaniment by Dean Crocker

can't jump o - ver! Two in the mid-dle and you can't jump o - ver!
can't jump o - ver! Four in the mid-dle and you can't jump o - ver!
I jump o - ver! Hold my__ mule_ while_ I jump o - ver!
B♭6
C7
F
Oh, Miss Su - san Brown!
We're Brown!
1., 2.
3.
F
C
F
F
mf

The Wee Falorie Man

PUPIL'S PAGE 375

Irish Folk Song
Collected by David Hammond
Piano Accompaniment by Dean Crocker

F
Dm
F
Dm
I am the wee Fa - lo - rie man, A
F/C
C7
F
F
rat - tlin', rov - in' I - rish-man, I can do all that ev - er you can, For
Dm
F
F
Dm
I am the wee Fa - lo - rie man.
F/C
C7
F
F/C
C7/E
F

Welcome Is the Month of May

PUPIL'S PAGE 378

Words and Music by Mary Donnelly
Piano Accompaniment by Dean Crocker

Joyous (♩. = 88)

C B♭M7 C C F G C

1. See the rob - in on the wing, bring - ing us a sign of spring. Flow - ers bloom - ing ev - 'ry-where; sweet per - fume_ will fill the air. Gone, the win - ter's bit - ter chill; time for tu - lip and daf - fo - dil. Sing a cheer - ful roun - de - lay.

2. When the hills are new - ly green, all the air is fresh and clean. Bum - ble - bee and but - ter - fly flit and flut - ter a - cross the sky. Gone, the win - ter's ice and snow. Time for flow - ers to bloom and grow. Sing a cheer - ful roun - de - lay.

F C C B♭M7 C C F C

C B♭M7 C Am G F C

Am G D G C F C

f *mf*

1.
Wel - come is the month of May!
Wel - come is the month of
C
B♭M7
G
C
B♭M7
C
C
F
f
2.
May!
G
Am7
CM7/G
F
G sus
G
C

What a Wonderful World

PUPIL'S PAGE 84

Words and Music by George David Weiss
and Bob Thiele
Piano Accompaniment by Dean Crocker

Rainbow gaze from L to R
world.
2. I see skies of blue and
FM7
A7(♯5)
Gm9
F♯dim
B♭/C
(♩. = ♩)
F(add9)/C
Am/C
p
clouds of white, the bright blessed day, the
Sway
L
R
B♭6
Am7
Gm7
F
mp
L
R
Stop
dark sacred night, and I think to myself What a wonderful
A7
Dm
D♭
Gm7
C7
world.
Yes, I think to myself,
F
Am7(♭5)/E♭
D7sus
D
Gm9
f

Look up
Smile
What a won - der - ful world.
B♭/C
C7
B♭M7
Dm7
D♭(add9)
E♭(add9)
F
3
mf
p

What Did Delaware?

PUPIL'S PAGE 190

American Folk Song
Piano Accompaniment by Dean Crocker

1.
2.
What did Del - a - ware? She
wore her New Jer - sey.
G/D
D7
G
G6
E♭9
D7
D dim
f
2. Why did Ca - li - phone ya? Why did Ca - li -
phoned to say "Ha - wa - ya." Phoned to say "Ha -
D7
G
C
mf
phone? Why did Ca - li - phone ya? Why did Ca - li -
wa - ya." She phoned to say "Ha - wa - ya." Phoned to say "Ha -
G
G
A7
phone? Why did Ca - li - phone ya? Why did Ca - li -
wa - ya." I phoned to say "Ha - wa - ya." Phoned to say "Ha -
D7
G
C

1.
phone? ask you as a friend of mine, Why did Ca - li - phone? She
wa - ya." I tell you as a friend of mine, She phoned to say "Ha -
G
Em
G/D
D7
G
2.
wa ya."
G6
E♭9
G
D dim
D7
D9
D7
G
f

Who Chopped the Cherry Tree Down?

PUPIL'S PAGE 371

Words and Music by Ruth Norman
Piano Accompaniment by Dean Crocker

Slower
Solo
All
Solo
down?
Who did? Who did? Who did? I did!
D
G D G D
G D G D
A Tempo
{He She} chopped the cher - ry tree down.
D/A D/F♯ F D/A A7
D
G A7/E Asus A D

Who Has the Penny?

PUPIL'S PAGE 252

Gently (♩ = 80)

American Singing Game
Piano Accompaniment by Dean Crocker

F(add2)

p

Question:

Who has the pen - ny?

F

Answer:

I have the pen - ny.

Question:

Who has the pin?

Answer:

I have the pin.

1.

F(add2)

2.
F(add 2)
3.
G(add 2)
4.
F(add 2)
F

Who's That Tapping at the Window?

PUPIL'S PAGE 261

American Singing Game
Piano Accompaniment by Dean Crocker

F
D7/F♯
Gm
C7
E
F
B♭/D
mf
f
1.
2.
D.S. al Coda
B♭m/D♭
C7
B♭/D
Cm7(♭5) C7
Coda
G7
ff

Willowbee

PUPIL'S PAGE 69

American Folk Song
Piano Accompaniment by Dean Crocker

B
Verse
Danc - ing down the al - ley, the al - ley, the al - ley, Danc - ing down the al - ley,
F Bb C F C F C F C7 F Bb C F Dm
All day long. Oh,
This way we wil - low - bee, oh,
Gm C7 F Bb(add9) C13 F
wil - low - bee, oh, wil - low - bee, This way we wil - low - bee, all day
Fsus/G BbM7 C9 C7 F C7
long.
F F C7 F

Yanai
(The Elephant)

PUPIL'S PAGE 305

16
kai kai kai ya ni mu ga til tum bik kei a du ve a dəɾ kə kai kai kai
as the Taj. Ro - yal look - ing as a ra-ja, Grand and glo - ri - ous as the Taj.
Coda
21
ya ni ya ni ya ni
Ya - nai, Ya - nai, Ya - nai.

Yankee Doodle

PUPIL'S PAGE 340

Traditional Melody
Words by Dr. Richard Shuckburgh
Piano Accompaniment by Dean Crocker

Refrain
Yan - kee Doo - dle keep it up, Yan - kee Doo - dle dan - dy,
D
A
Mind the mu - sic and the step, and with the girls be han - dy.
D
A/E
E7
A

You Are My Sunshine

PUPIL'S PAGE 369

Words and Music by Jimmie Davis and Charles Mitchell
Piano Accompaniment by Dean Crocker

Lean L with hands to heart
Lean R
know, Dear, how much I love you, Please don't
B♭
F
B♭/D D♭dim7
Wiggle jazz jands by face
Big smile
take my sun - shine a - way.
F
C7
F
f
F
B♭
F
3

B♭
F
B♭/D D♭dim7
F
C7
F
Wiggle jazz hands by face
You are my sun - shine, my on - ly sun - shine.
C7
F
mf
1 clap burst
Rain hands
You make me hap - py when skies are gray.
B♭
F

Lean L with hands to heart
_ You'll nev - er know, Dear, how much I
B♭
Lean R
Wiggle jazz jands by face
love you, Please don't take my
F
B♭/D D♭dim7
F
Big smile
sun - shine a - way.
C7
F
C
C7
Dm7
G9
C7
F

You'll Sing a Song and I'll Sing a Song

PUPIL'S PAGE 156

Words and Music by Ella Jenkins
Piano Accompaniment by Dean Crocker

I'll sing a song, in warm or win - try weath - er.
Dm7
G6
Dm7
G7
Dm7
F/G
1.
C
Am7
Dm7
G7
C
Am7
2.
Dm7
F/G
C
Am7
Dm7
F/G
G/B
C

You've Got a Friend in Me

from the movie *Toy Story*

PUPIL'S PAGE 44

Words and Music by Randy Newman
Piano Accompaniment by Dean Crocker

Point index fingers at audience
Thumbs to self
Point index fingers at aud.
old pal said. Son, you've got a friend in me. Yeah, you've
see it through, 'cause you've got a friend in me. Yeah, you've
E7 Am D7 F/G C A7 A7(♯9)
Thumbs to self
got a friend in me.
got a friend in me.
1.
D7 F/G C E7/B Am7 A♭7
2.
C/G Cdim/G Ddim/G C E7/B
f
Thumbs up to audience
Am7 A♭7 C/G Cdim/G Ddim/G C9
f

Acknowledgements

Grateful acknowledgement is given to the following authors, composers, and publishers. Every effort has been made to trace the ownership of all copyrighted material and to secure the necessary permissions to reprint these selections. In the case of some selections for which acknowledgment is not given, extensive research has failed to locate the copyright holders.

Apple Picker's Reel, Words and Music by Larry Hanks. Copyright © 1967. Alpha Film Music. International Copyright Secured. All Rights Reserved.

Artichokes, Words and Music by Malvina Reynolds. Copyright © Schroder Music Company. International Copyright Secured. All Rights Reserved.

Baby Beluga, Words and Music by Raffi Cavoukian and D. Pike. Copyright © 1980 by Homeland Publishing, a div. of Troubadour Music, Inc. International Copyright Secured. All Rights Reserved.

Ban Dal (Half Moon), Words and Music by Keuk Young Youn. Copyright © by SEH KWANG PUBLISHING CO. International Copyright Secured. All Rights Reserved.

Big Beautiful Planet, Words and Music by Raffi Cavoukian. Copyright © by Homeland Publishing, a div. of Troubadour Music, Inc. International Copyright Secured. All Rights Reserved.

Candle on the Water, from Walt Disney's *PETE'S DRAGON.* Words and Music by Al Kasha and Joel Hirschhorn. Copyright © 1976 Walt Disney Music Company and Wonderland Music Company, Inc. All Rights Reserved. Used by Permission.

Check It Out! (It's About Respect), Words and Music by John Jacobson and John Higgins. Copyright © 2001 by MUSIC EXPRESS LLC. International Copyright Secured. All Rights Reserved.

Columbus Sailed with Three Ships, Words and Music by Margaret Campbelle-Holman. Copyright © 1981 by Margaret Campbelle-Holman. International Copyright Secured. All Rights Reserved.

Dal taro kacha (Come, Pick the Moon), Words by Suk-Joong Yoon. Music by Tae-Hyun Park, Copyright © by SHE KWANG PUBLISHING CO. International Copyright Secured. All Rights Reserved.

Dance, Dance, Dance!, Words by Ava Hogan Chapman. Music by Moses Hogan. Copyright © 2001 by MUSIC EXPRESS LLC. International Copyright Secured. All Rights Reserved.

Eating Lizards, Words and Music by Carol Huffman.

El burrito enfermo (The Sick Little Donkey), Latin American Folk Song. Adapted by José-Luis Orozco. Copyright © by José-Luis Orozco/Arcoiris Records, P.O. Box 461900, Los Angeles, CA 90046. International Copyright Secured. All Rights Reserved.

El palomo y la paloma (The Doves), Mexican Folk Song. Adapted by José-Luis Orozco. Copyright © 1996 by José-Luis Orozco/Arcoiris Records, P.O. Box 461900, Los Angeles, CA 90046. International Copyright Secured. All Rights Reserved.

En nuestra Tierra tan linda (On Our Beautiful Planet Earth), Latin American Folk Song. Adapted by José-Luis Orozco. Copyright © 1996 by José-Luis Orozco/Arcoiris Records, P.O. Box 461900, Los Angeles, CA 90046. International Copyright Secured. All Rights Reserved.

Everybody Has Music Inside, Words and Music by Greg Scelsa. Copyright © 1980 Little House Music (ASCAP). International Copyright Secured. All Rights Reserved.

Everything Grows, Words and Music by Raffi Cavoukian and D. Pike. Copyright © 1987 by Homeland Publishing, a div. of Troubadour Music, Inc. International Copyright Secured. All Rights Reserved.

Food Song, The, Words and Music by Jackie Silberg. Copyright © 1989 by Miss Jackie Music Company. International Copyright Secured. All Rights Reserved.

Garden Song, Words and Music by Dave Mallett. Copyright © 1975. Cherry Lane Music Publishing Company, Inc. (ASCAP) and DreamWorks Songs (ASCAP). Worldwide Rights for DreamWorks Songs Administered by Cherry Lane Music Publishing Company, Inc. International Copyright Secured. All Rights Reserved.

Great Outdoors, The, from Disneyland and Walt Disney World's *COUNTRY BEAR JAMBOREE.* Words and Music by George Wilkins. © 1988. Walt Disney Music Company. All Rights Reserved. Used by Permission.

Green Eggs and Ham, from MTI's Broadway Junior Broadway for Kids SEUSSICAL Junior. Music by Stephen Flaherty. Lyrics by Lynn Ahrens. Copyright © 2001 by Warner Chappell Publishing Co., Inc., Hillsdale Music, Inc., Pen and Perseverance, Inc.

Hakuna Matata, from Walt Disney Pictures' *THE LION KING*. Music by Elton John. Lyrics by Tim Rice. © 1994. Wonderland Music Company, Inc. All Rights Reserved. Used by Permission.

Hello, Hello There, Words by Betty Comden and Adolph Green. Music by Jule Styne. Copyright © 1956 by Stratford Music Corporation. Copyright Renewed. All Rights Administered by Chappell & Co. International Copyright Secured. All Rights Reserved.

Horton Hears a Who!, from MTI's Broadway Junior Broadway for Kids SEUSSICAL Junior. Music by Stephen Flaherty. Lyrics by Lynn Ahrens. Copyright © 2001 by Warner Chappell Publishing Co., Inc., Hillsdale Music, Inc., Pen and Perseverance, Inc.

Horton Hears a Who! Two, from MTI's Broadway Junior Broadway for Kids SEUSSICAL Junior. Music by Stephen Flaherty. Lyrics by Lynn Ahrens. Copyright © 2001 by Warner Chappell Publishing Co., Inc., Hillsdale Music, Inc., Pen and Perseverance, Inc.

It's a Small World, from *"it's a small world"* at Disneyland Park and Magic Kingdom. Words and Music by Richard M. Sherman and Robert B. Sherman. Copyright © 1963. Wonderland Music Company, Inc. Copyright Renewed. All Rights Reserved. Used by Permission.

It's Possible, from MTI's Broadway Junior Broadway for Kids SEUSSICAL Junior. Music by Stephen Flaherty. Lyrics by Lynn Ahrens. Copyright © 2001 by Warner Chappell Publishing Co., Inc., Hillsdale Music, Inc., Pen and Perseverance, Inc.

Joy, from *THE FEEL OF MUSIC*, Words and Music by Hap Palmer. Copyright © by Hap-Pal Music, Inc. International Copyright Secured. All Rights Reserved.

Jugaremos en el bosque (We Will Play in the Forest), from *LIRICA INFANTIL DE MEXICO*. By Vicente T. Mendoza. Copyright © 1980 by Fondo De Cultura Economica, Av. de la Universidad 975, 03100 Mexico, D.F. International Copyright Secured. All Rights Reserved.

Let's Go Fly a Kite, from Walt Disney's *MARY POPPINS*. Words and Music by Richard M. Sherman and Robert B. Sherman. Copyright © 1963 Wonderland Music Company, Inc. Copyright Renewed. All Rights Reserved. Used by Permission.

Mama Paquita, Brazilian Carnival Song, English Version by Merrill Staton. Copyright © 1986 by Rockhaven Music. International Copyright Secured. All Rights Reserved.

Martin Luther King, Words and Music by Mary Donnelly and George L.O. Strid. Copyright © 2002 by HAL LEONARD CORPORATION. International Copyright Secured. All Rights Reserved.

Merry-Go-Round, Words by Dorothy Baruch. Arranged by Marilyn Davidson. Copyright © 1952, 1961 (Renewed 1980, 1989) by Scott Foresman & Company, International Copyright Secured. All Rights Reserved.

Oh, the Thinks You Can Think!, from MTI's Broadway Junior Broadway for Kids SEUSSICAL Junior. Music by Stephen Flaherty. Lyrics by Lynn Ahrens. Copyright © 2001 by Warner Chappell Publishing Co., Inc., Hillsdale Music, Inc., Pen and Perseverance, Inc.

On Top of Spaghetti, Words and Music by Tom Glazer. Copyright © 1963, 1965 by Songs Music Inc. Copyright Renewed. Administered in the United States and Canada by September Music Corp. International Copyright Secured. All Rights Reserved.

Part of Your World, from Walt Disney's *THE LITTLE MERMAID*. Lyrics by Howard Ashman. Music by Alan Menken. Copyright © 1988 Walt Disney Music Company and Wonderland Music Company, Inc. All Rights Reserved. Used by Permission.

Pick a Pumpkin, Words and Music by Naomi Caldwell. Copyright © 1965, 1970 (Renewed 1993,1998) by Ginn & Company. International Copyright Secured. All Rights Reserved. Used by Permission of Silver, Burdett & Ginn, Inc.

Place in The Choir, A, Words and Music by Bill Staines. Copyright © 1978 Mineral River Music (BMI). Rights Administered by Bug Music Inc. International Copyright Secured. All Rights Reserved.

Puff the Magic Dragon, Words and Music by Lenny Lipton and Peter Yarrow. Copyright © 1963. Renewed 1991. Honalee Melodies (ASCAP) and Silver Dawn Music (ASCAP). Worldwide Rights for Honalee Melodies Administered by Cherry Lane Music Publishing Company, Inc. Worldwide Rights for Silver Dawn Music Administered by WB Music Corp. International Copyright Secured. All Rights Reserved.

Sailor, Sailor on the Sea, Words and Music by Jean Ritchie. Copyright © by Jean Ritchie/Geordie Music Publishing Co. International Copyright Secured. All Rights Reserved. Used by Permission.

Seeds and Seasons, Words and Music by Jim Walters. Copyright © Jim Walters. International Copyright Secured. All Rights Reserved.

Seussical Mega-Mix, from MTI's Broadway Junior Broadway for Kids SEUSSICAL Junior. Music by Stephen Flaherty. Lyrics by Lynn Ahrens. Copyright © 2001 by Warner Chappell Publishing Co., Inc., Hillsdale Music, Inc., Pen and Perseverance, Inc.

Shrimp Boats, Words and Music by Paul Mason Howard and Paul Weston. Copyright © 1951. Walt Disney Music Company, Copyright Renewed 1979. Walt Disney Music Company and Hanover Music Corporation. All Rights Reserved. Used by Permission.

Sing! Sing! Sing!, Words and Music by Branice McKenzie. Copyright © 2002 by Eunice Music. International Copyright Secured. All Rights Reserved.

Skating, Words and Music by Lynn Freeman Olson and Georgia Garlid. Copyright © 1968. (Renewed 1996). EMI MILLS MUSIC INC. All Rights Controlled by EMI MILLS MUSIC INC. (Publishing) and WARNER BROS. PUBLICATIONS U.S. INC. (Print). All Rights Reserved. Used by Permission.

Step in Time, from Walt Disney's *MARY POPPINS*. Words and Music by Richard M. Sherman and Robert B. Sherman. Copyright © 1963 Wonderland Music Company, Inc. Copyright Renewed. All Rights Reserved. Used by Permission.

This Is Halloween, Words and Music by Teresa Jennings. Copyright © 2001 by Plank Road Publishing. International Copyright Secured. All Rights Reserved.

This Is My Country, Words by Don Raye. Music by Al Jacobs. Copyright © 1940 SHAWNEE PRESS. INC. Copyright © Renewed SHAWNEE PRESS, INC. and WAROCK CORP. All Rights Reserved.

Tiki Tiki Room, The, from E*NCHANTED TIKI ROOM* at Disneyland Park and *TROPICAL SERENADE*. Words and Music by Richard M. Sherman and Robert B. Sherman. Copyright © 1963 Wonderland Music Company, Inc. Copyright Renewed. All Rights Reserved. Used by Permission.

Wake Up the Sun, Words and Music by John Jacobson and Emily Crocker. Copyright © 2000 by HAL LEONARD CORPORATION. International Copyright Secured. All Rights Reserved.

Welcome Is the Month Of May, Words and Music by Mary Donnelly and George L.O. Strid. Copyright © 1999 by HAL LEONARD CORPORATION. International Copyright Secured. All Rights Reserved.

What a Wonderful World, Words and Music by George David Weiss and Bob Thiele. Copyright © 1967 by Range Road Music Inc., Quartet Music, Inc. and Abilene Music, Inc. Copyright Renewed. International Copyright Secured. All Rights Reserved. Used by Permission.

Who Chopped the Cherry Tree Down?, Words and Music by Ruth Norman. Copyright © 1952 (Renewed 1980). EMI MILLS MUSIC INC. All Rights Controlled by EMI MILLS MUSIC INC. (Publishing) and WARNER BROS. PUBLICATIONS U.S. INC. (Print). All Rights Reserved. Used by Permission.

You Are My Sunshine, Words and Music by Jimmie Davis and Charles Mitchell. Copyright © 1930 by Peer International Corporation. Copyright Renewed. International Copyright Secured. All Rights Reserved.

You'll Sing a Song and I'll Sing a Song, Words and Music by Ella Jenkins. Copyright © by Ell-Bern Publishing Company. International Copyright Secured. All Rights Reserved.

You've Got a Friend in Me, from Walt Disney's *TOY STORY*. Music and Lyrics by Randy Newman. Copyright © 1995. Walt Disney Music Company. All Rights Reserved. Used by Permission.

Teacher's Notes

Teacher's Notes

Teacher's Notes

Teacher's Notes

Teacher's Notes

Teacher's Notes

Alphabetical Song Index